chapter

6

The Three-Dimensional Structure of Proteins

The covalent backbone of a typical protein contains hundreds of individual bonds. Because free rotation is possible around many of these bonds, the protein can assume an unlimited number of conformations. However, each protein has a specific chemical or structural function, strongly suggesting that each has a unique three-dimensional structure (Fig. 6–1). By the late 1920s, several proteins had been crystallized, including hemoglobin (M_r 64,500) and the enzyme urease (M_r 483,000). Given that the ordered array of molecules in a crystal can generally form only if the molecular units are identical, the simple fact that many proteins can be crystallized provides strong evidence that even very large proteins are discrete chemical entities with unique structures. This conclusion revolutionized thinking about proteins and their functions.

In this chapter, we will explore the three-dimensional structure of proteins, emphasizing five themes. First, the three-dimensional structure of a protein is determined by its amino acid sequence. Second, the function of a protein depends on its structure. Third, an isolated protein has a unique, or nearly unique, structure. Fourth, the most important forces stabilizing the specific structure maintained by a given protein are noncovalent interactions. Finally, amid the huge number of unique protein structures, we can recognize some common structural patterns that help us organize our understanding of protein architecture.

These themes should not be taken to imply that proteins have static, unchanging three-dimensional structures. Protein function often entails an interconversion between two or more structural forms. The dynamic aspects of protein structure will be explored in later chapters.

The relationship between the amino acid sequence of a protein and its three-dimensional structure is an intricate puzzle that is gradually yielding to techniques used in modern biochemistry. An understanding of structure, in turn, is essential to the discussion of function in succeeding chapters. We can find and understand the patterns within the biochemical labyrinth of protein structure by applying fundamental principles of chemistry and physics.

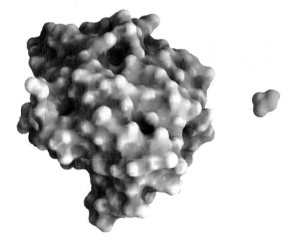

figure 6–1
Structure of the enzyme chymotrypsin, a globular protein. Proteins are large molecules, and we will see that each has a unique structure. A molecule of glycine (blue) is shown for size comparison.

Overview of Protein Structure

The spatial arrangement of atoms in a protein is called its **conformation.** The possible conformations of a protein include any structural state that can be achieved without breaking covalent bonds. A change in conformation could occur, for example, by rotation about single bonds. Of the numerous conformations that are theoretically possible in a protein containing hundreds of single bonds, one or a few generally predominate under biological conditions. The conformation existing under a given set of conditions is usually the one that is thermodynamically the most stable, having the lowest Gibbs free energy (G). Proteins in any of their functional, folded conformations are called **native** proteins.

What principles determine the most stable conformation of a protein? An understanding of protein conformation can be built stepwise from the discussion of primary structure in Chapter 5, through a consideration of secondary, tertiary, and quaternary structure. To this traditional approach must be added a new emphasis on supersecondary structures, a growing set of known and classifiable protein folding patterns that provides an important organizational context to this complex endeavor. We begin by introducing some guiding principles.

A Protein's Conformation Is Stabilized Largely by Weak Interactions

In the context of protein structure, the term **stability** can be defined as the tendency to maintain a native conformation. Native proteins are only marginally stable; the ΔG separating the folded and unfolded states in typical proteins under physiological conditions is in the range of only 20 to 65 kJ/mol. A given polypeptide chain can theoretically assume countless different conformations, and as a result the unfolded state of a protein is characterized by a high degree of conformational entropy. This entropy, and the hydrogen-bonding interactions of many groups in the polypeptide chain with solvent (water), tend to maintain the unfolded state. The chemical interactions that counteract these effects and stabilize the native conformation include disulfide bonds and weak (noncovalent) interactions described in Chapter 4: hydrogen bonds, and hydrophobic and ionic interactions. An appreciation of the role of these weak interactions is especially important to our understanding of how polypeptide chains fold into specific secondary and tertiary structures, and combine with other proteins to form quaternary structures.

About 200 to 460 kJ/mol are required to break a single covalent bond, whereas weak interactions can be disrupted by a mere 4 to 30 kJ/mol. Individual covalent bonds that contribute to the native conformations of proteins, such as disulfide bonds linking separate parts of a single polypeptide chain, are clearly much stronger than individual weak interactions, yet it is weak interactions that predominate as a stabilizing force in protein structure because they are so numerous. In general, the protein conformation with the lowest free energy (i.e., the most stable conformation) is the one with the maximum number of weak interactions.

The stability of a protein is not simply the sum of the free energies of formation of the many weak interactions within it. Every hydrogen-bonding group in a folded polypeptide chain was hydrogen bonded to water prior to folding, and for every hydrogen bond formed in a protein, a hydrogen bond (of similar strength) between the same group and water was broken. The net stability contributed by a given weak interaction, or the *difference* in free energies of the folded and unfolded states, may be close to zero. We must therefore look elsewhere to explain why the native conformation of a protein is favored.

We find that the contribution of weak interactions to protein stability can be understood in terms of the properties of water (Chapter 4). Pure water contains a network of hydrogen-bonded H_2O molecules. No other molecule has the hydrogen-bonding potential of water, and other molecules present in an aqueous solution disrupt the hydrogen bonding of water. When water surrounds a hydrophobic molecule, the optimal arrangement of hydrogen bonds results in a highly structured shell or **solvation layer** of water in the immediate vicinity. The increased order of the water molecules in the solvation layer correlates with an unfavorable decrease in the entropy of the water. However, when nonpolar groups are clustered together, there is a decrease in the extent of the solvation layer because each group no longer presents its entire surface to the solution. The result is a favorable increase in entropy. As described in Chapter 4, this entropy term is the major thermodynamic driving force for the association of hydrophobic groups in aqueous solution. Hydrophobic amino acid side chains therefore tend to be clustered in a protein's interior, away from water.

Under physiological conditions, the formation of hydrogen bonds and ionic interactions in a protein is driven largely by this same entropic effect. Polar groups can generally form hydrogen bonds with water and hence are soluble in water. However, the number of hydrogen bonds per unit mass is generally greater for pure water than for any other liquid or solution, and there are limits to the solubility of even the most polar molecules because their presence causes a net decrease in hydrogen bonding per unit mass. Therefore, a solvation shell of structured water will also form to some extent around polar molecules. Even though the energy of formation of an intramolecular hydrogen bond or ionic interaction between two polar groups in a macromolecule is largely canceled out by the elimination of such interactions between the same groups and water, the release of structured water when the intramolecular interaction is formed provides an entropic driving force for folding. Most of the net change in free energy that occurs when weak interactions are formed within a protein is therefore derived from the increased entropy in the surrounding aqueous solution resulting from the burial of hydrophobic surfaces. This more than counterbalances the large loss of conformational entropy as a polypeptide is constrained into a single folded conformation.

Hydrophobic interactions are clearly important in stabilizing a protein conformation; the interior of a protein is generally a densely packed core of hydrophobic amino acid side chains. It is also important that any polar or charged groups in the protein interior have suitable partners for hydrogen bonding or ionic interactions. One hydrogen bond seems to contribute little to the stability of a native structure, but the presence of hydrogen-bonding or charged groups without partners in the hydrophobic core of a protein can be so *destabilizing* that conformations containing such a group are often thermodynamically untenable. The favorable free-energy change realized by combining such a group with a partner in the surrounding solution can be greater than the difference in free energy between the folded and unfolded states. In addition, hydrogen bonds between groups in proteins form cooperatively. Formation of one hydrogen bond facilitates the formation of additional hydrogen bonds. The overall contribution of hydrogen bonds and other noncovalent interactions to the stabilization of protein conformation is still being evaluated. The interaction of oppositely charged groups that form an ion pair (salt bridge) may also have a stabilizing effect on one or more native conformations of some proteins.

Most of the structural patterns outlined in this chapter reflect two simple rules: (1) hydrophobic residues are largely buried in the protein interior, away from water, and (2) the number of hydrogen bonds within the protein is maximized. Insoluble proteins and proteins within membranes follow somewhat different rules because of their function or their environment, but weak interactions are still critical structural elements.

Linus Pauling
1901–1994

Robert Corey
1897–1971

The Peptide Bond Is Rigid and Planar

Covalent bonds also place important constraints on the conformation of a polypeptide. In the late 1930s, Linus Pauling and Robert Corey embarked on a series of studies that laid the foundation for our present understanding of protein structure. They began with a careful analysis of the peptide bond. The α carbons of adjacent amino acid residues are separated by three covalent bonds, arranged as C_α—C—N—C_α. X-ray diffraction studies of crystals of amino acids and of simple dipeptides and tripeptides demonstrated that the peptide C—N bond is somewhat shorter than the C—N bond in a simple amine and that the atoms associated with the peptide bond are coplanar. This indicated a resonance or partial sharing of two pairs of electrons between the carbonyl oxygen and the amide nitrogen (Fig. 6–2a). The oxygen has a partial negative charge and the nitrogen a partial positive charge, setting up a small electric dipole. The six atoms of the **peptide group** lie in a single plane, with the oxygen atom of the carbonyl group and the hydrogen atom of the amide nitrogen trans to each other. From these findings Pauling and Corey concluded that the peptide C—N bonds are unable to rotate freely because of their partial double-bond character. Rotation is permitted about the N—C_α and the C_α—C bonds. The backbone of a polypeptide chain can thus be pictured as a series of rigid planes with consecutive planes sharing a common point of rotation at C_α (Fig. 6–2b). The

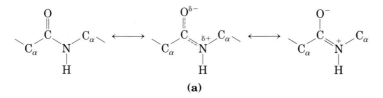

The carbonyl oxygen has a partial negative charge and the amide nitrogen a partial positive charge, setting up a small electric dipole. Virtually all peptide bonds in proteins occur in this trans configuration; an exception is noted in Figure 6–8b.

(a)

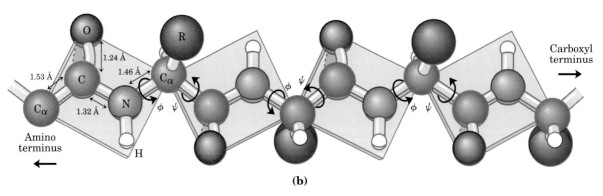

(b)

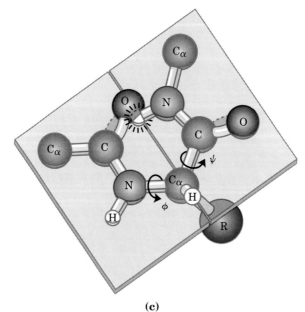

(c)

figure 6–2

The planar peptide group. (a) Each peptide bond has some double-bond character due to resonance and cannot rotate. **(b)** Three bonds separate sequential α carbons in a polypeptide chain. The N—C_α and C_α—C bonds can rotate, with bond angles designated φ and ψ, respectively. The peptide C—N bond is not free to rotate. Other single bonds in the backbone may also be rotationally hindered, depending on the size and charge of the R groups. **(c)** By convention, φ and ψ are both defined as 0° when the two peptide bonds flanking that α carbon are in the same plane and positioned as shown. In a protein, this conformation is prohibited by steric overlap between an α-carbonyl oxygen and an α-amino hydrogen atom. To illustrate the bonds between atoms, the balls representing each atom are smaller than the van der Waals radii for this scale. 1 Å = 0.1 nm.

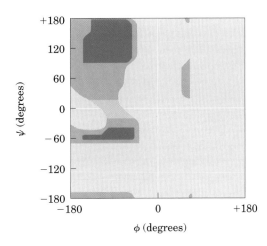

figure 6–3
Ramachandran plot for L-Ala residues. The conformations of peptides are defined by the values of ϕ and ψ. Conformations deemed possible are those that involve little or no steric interference, based on calculations using known van der Waals radii and bond angles. The areas shaded dark blue reflect conformations that involve no steric overlap and thus are fully allowed; medium blue indicates conformations allowed at the extreme limits for unfavorable atomic contacts; the lightest blue area reflects conformations that are permissible if a little flexibility is allowed in the bond angles. The asymmetry of the plot results from the L stereochemistry of the amino acid residues. The plots for other L-amino acid residues with unbranched side chains are nearly identical. The allowed ranges for branched amino acid residues such as Val, Ile, and Thr are somewhat smaller than for Ala. The Gly residue, which is less sterically hindered, exhibits a much broader range of allowed conformations. The range for Pro residues is greatly restricted because ϕ is limited by the cyclic side chain to the range of $-35°$ to $-85°$.

rigid peptide bonds limit the range of conformations that can be assumed by a polypeptide chain.

By convention the bond angles resulting from rotations at C_α are labeled ϕ (phi) for the $N—C_\alpha$ bond and ψ (psi) for the $C_\alpha—C$ bond. Again by convention, both ϕ and ψ are defined as 180° when the polypeptide is in its fully extended conformation and all peptide groups are in the same plane (Fig. 6–2b). In principle, ϕ and ψ can have any value between $-180°$ and $+180°$, but many values are prohibited by steric interference between atoms in the polypeptide backbone and amino acid side chains. The conformation in which both ϕ and ψ are 0° (Fig. 6–2c) is prohibited for this reason; this is used merely as a reference point for describing the angles of rotation. Allowed values for ϕ and ψ are graphically revealed when ψ is plotted versus ϕ in a **Ramachandran plot** (Fig. 6–3), introduced by G.N. Ramachandran.

Protein Secondary Structure

The term **secondary structure** refers to the local conformation of some part of the polypeptide. The discussion of secondary structure most usefully focuses on common regular folding patterns of the polypeptide backbone. A few types of secondary structure are particularly stable and occur widely in proteins. The most prominent are the α helix and β conformations described below. Using fundamental chemical principles and a few experimental observations, Pauling and Corey predicted the existence of these secondary structures in 1951, several years before the first complete protein structure was elucidated.

The α Helix Is a Common Protein Secondary Structure

Pauling and Corey were aware of the importance of hydrogen bonds in orienting polar chemical groups such as the $C{=}O$ and $N—H$ groups of the peptide bond. They also had the experimental results of William Astbury, who in the 1930s had conducted pioneering x-ray studies of proteins. Astbury demonstrated that the protein that makes up hair and porcupine quills (the fibrous protein α-keratin) has a regular structure that repeats every 5.15 to 5.2 Å. (The angstrom, Å (named after the physicist Anders J. Ångström), is equal to 0.1 nm. Although not an SI unit, it is used universally by structural biologists to describe atomic distances.) With this information and their data on the peptide bond, and with the help of precisely constructed models, Pauling and Corey set out to determine the likely conformations of protein molecules.

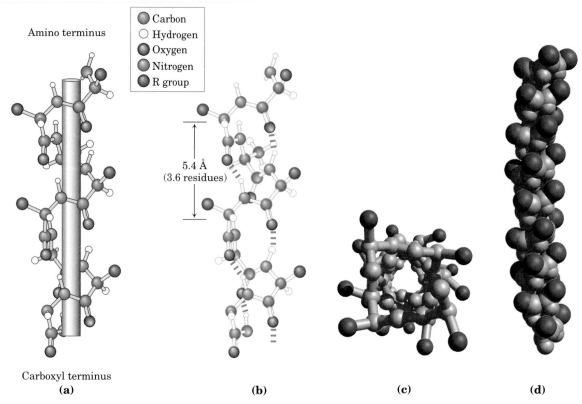

Amino terminus

	Carbon
○	Hydrogen
	Oxygen
	Nitrogen
	R group

5.4 Å
(3.6 residues)

Carboxyl terminus

(a)   **(b)**   **(c)**   **(d)**

figure 6–4

Four models of the α helix, showing different aspects of its structure. (a) Formation of a right-handed α helix. The planes of the rigid peptide bonds are parallel to the long axis of the helix, depicted here as a vertical rod. **(b)** Ball-and-stick model of a right-handed α helix, showing the intrachain hydrogen bonds. The repeat unit is a single turn of the helix, 3.6 residues. **(c)** The α helix as viewed from one end, looking down the longitudinal axis. Note the positions of the R groups, represented by purple spheres. This ball-and-stick model, used to emphasize the helical arrangement, gives the false impression that the helix is hollow because the balls do not represent the van der Waals radii of the individual atoms. As the space-filling model **(d)** shows, the atoms in the center of the α helix are in very close contact.

The simplest arrangement the polypeptide chain could assume with its rigid peptide bonds (but other single bonds free to rotate) is a helical structure, which Pauling and Corey called the **α helix** (Fig. 6–4). In this structure the polypeptide backbone is tightly wound around an imaginary axis drawn longitudinally through the middle of the helix, and the R groups of the amino acid residues protrude outward from the helical backbone. The repeating unit is a single turn of the helix, which extends about 5.4 Å along the long axis, slightly greater than the periodicity Astbury observed on x-ray analysis of hair keratin. The amino acid residues in an α helix have conformations with $\psi = -45°$ to $-50°$ and $\phi = -60°$, and each helical turn includes 3.6 amino acid residues. The helical twist of the α helix found in all proteins is right-handed (Box 6–1). The α helix proved to be the predominant structure in α-keratins. More generally, about one-fourth of all amino acid residues in polypeptides are found in α helices, the exact fraction varying greatly from one protein to the next.

Why does the α helix form more readily than many other possible conformations? The answer is, in part, that an α helix makes optimal use of internal hydrogen bonds. The structure is stabilized by a hydrogen bond between the hydrogen atom attached to the electronegative nitrogen atom of a peptide linkage and the electronegative carbonyl oxygen atom of the fourth amino acid on the amino-terminal side of that peptide bond (Fig. 6–4b). Within the α helix, every peptide bond (except those close to each end of the helix) participates in such hydrogen bonding. Each successive turn of the α helix is held to adjacent turns by three to four hydrogen bonds. All the hydrogen bonds combined give the entire helical structure considerable stability.

Further model-building experiments have shown that an α helix can form in polypeptides consisting of either L- or D-amino acids. However, all residues must be of one stereoisomeric series; a D-amino acid will disrupt a

box 6-1 | Knowing the Right Hand from the Left

There is a simple method for determining whether a helical structure is right-handed or left-handed. Make fists of your two hands with thumbs outstretched and pointing straight up. Looking at your right hand, think of a helix spiraling up your right thumb in the direction in which the other four fingers are curled as shown (counterclockwise). The resulting helix is right-handed. Your left hand will demonstrate a left-handed helix, which rotates in the clockwise direction as it spirals up your thumb.

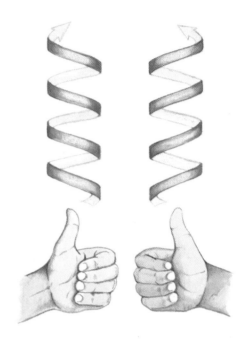

regular structure consisting of L-amino acids, and vice versa. Naturally occurring L-amino acids can form either right- or left-handed α helices, but extended left-handed helices have not been observed in proteins.

Amino Acid Sequence Affects α Helix Stability

Not all polypeptides can form a stable α helix. Interactions between amino acid side chains can stabilize or destabilize this structure. For example, if a polypeptide chain has a long block of Glu residues, this segment of the chain will not form an α helix at pH 7.0. The negatively charged carboxyl groups of adjacent Glu residues repel each other so strongly that they overcome the stabilizing influence of hydrogen bonds on the α helix. For the same reason, if there are many adjacent Lys and/or Arg residues, which have positively charged R groups at pH 7.0, they will also repel each other and prevent formation of the α helix. The bulk and shape of Asn, Ser, Thr, and Leu residues can also destabilize an α helix if they are close together in the chain.

The twist of an α helix ensures that critical interactions occur between an amino acid side chain and the side chain three (and sometimes four) residues away on either side of it (Fig. 6–5). Positively charged amino acids are often found three residues away from negatively charged amino acids, permitting the formation of an ion pair. Two aromatic amino acid residues are often similarly spaced, resulting in a hydrophobic interaction.

A constraint on the formation of the α helix is the presence of Pro or Gly residues. In proline, the nitrogen atom is part of a rigid ring (see Fig. 6–8b), and rotation about the N—C_α bond is not possible. Thus, a Pro residue introduces a destabilizing kink in an α helix. In addition, the nitrogen atom of a Pro residue in peptide linkage has no substituent hydrogen to participate in hydrogen bonds with other residues. For these reasons, proline is only

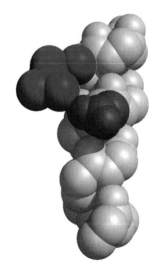

figure 6–5

Interactions between R groups of amino acids three residues apart in an α helix. An ionic interaction between Asp[100] and Arg[103] in an α-helical region of the protein troponin C, a calcium-binding protein associated with muscle, is shown in this space-filling model. The polypeptide backbone (carbons, α-amino nitrogens, and α-carbonyl oxygens) is shown in gray for a helix segment 13 residues long. The only side chains represented here are the interacting Asp (red) and Arg (blue) residues.

Amino terminus

δ^+

Carboxyl terminus

figure 6–6
The electric dipole of a peptide bond (see Fig. 6–2a) is transmitted along an α-helical segment through the intra-chain hydrogen bonds, resulting in an overall helix dipole. In this illustration, the amino and carbonyl constituents of each peptide bond are indicated by + and − symbols, respectively. Non-hydrogen-bonded amino and carbonyl constituents in the peptide bonds near each end of the α-helical region are shown in red.

rarely found within an α helix. Glycine occurs infrequently in α helices for a different reason: it has more conformational flexibility than the other amino acid residues. Polymers of glycine tend to take up coiled structures quite different from an α helix.

A final factor affecting the stability of an α helix in a polypeptide is the identity of the amino acid residues near the ends of the α-helical segment. A small electric dipole exists in each peptide bond (Fig. 6–2a). These dipoles are connected through the hydrogen bonds of the helix, resulting in a net dipole extending down the helix that increases with helix length (Fig. 6–6). The four amino acid residues at each end of the helix do not participate fully in the helix hydrogen bonds. The partial positive and negative charges of the helix dipole actually reside on the peptide amino and carbonyl groups near the amino-terminal and carboxyl-terminal ends of the helix, respectively. For this reason, negatively charged amino acids are often found near the amino terminus of the helical segment, where they have a stabilizing interaction with the positive charge of the helix dipole; a positively charged amino acid at the amino-terminal end is destabilizing. The opposite is true at the carboxyl-terminal end of the helical segment.

Thus five different kinds of constraints affect the stability of an α helix: (1) the electrostatic repulsion (or attraction) between successive amino acid residues with charged R groups, (2) the bulkiness of adjacent R groups, (3) the interactions between amino acid side chains spaced three (or four) residues apart, (4) the occurrence of Pro and Gly residues, and (5) the interaction between amino acid residues at the ends of the helical segment and the electric dipole inherent to the α helix. Hence, the tendency of a given segment of a polypeptide chain to fold up as an α helix depends on the identity and sequence of amino acid residues within the segment.

The β Conformation Organizes Polypeptide Chains into Sheets

Pauling and Corey predicted a second type of repetitive structure, the **β conformation.** This is a more extended conformation of polypeptide chains, and its structure has been confirmed by x-ray analysis. In the β conformation, the backbone of the polypeptide chain is extended into a zigzag rather than helical structure (Fig. 6–7). The zigzag polypeptide chains can be arranged side by side to form a structure resembling a series of pleats. In this arrangement, called a **β sheet,** hydrogen bonds are formed between adjacent segments of polypeptide chain. The individual segments that form a β sheet are usually nearby on the polypeptide chain, but can also be quite distant from each other in the linear sequence of the polypeptide; they may even be segments in different polypeptide chains. The R groups of adjacent amino acids protrude from the zigzag structure in opposite directions, creating an alternating pattern as seen in the side views in Figure 6–7.

The adjacent polypeptide chains in a β sheet can be either parallel or antiparallel (having the same or opposite amino-to-carboxyl orientations, respectively). The structures are somewhat similar, although the repeat period is shorter for the parallel conformation (6.5 Å, versus 7 Å for antiparallel) and the hydrogen-bonding patterns are different.

Some protein structures limit the kinds of amino acids that can occur in the β sheet. When two or more β sheets are layered closely together within a protein, the R groups of the amino acid residues on the touching surfaces must be relatively small. β-Keratins such as silk fibroin and the fibroin of spider webs have a very high content of Gly and Ala residues, the two amino acids with the smallest R groups. Indeed, in silk fibroin Gly and Ala alternate over large parts of the sequence.

(a) Antiparallel

Top view

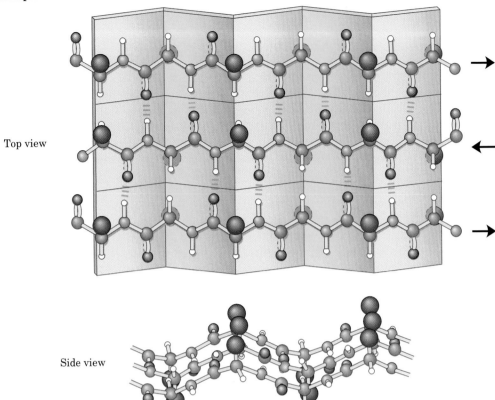

Side view

(b) Parallel

Top view

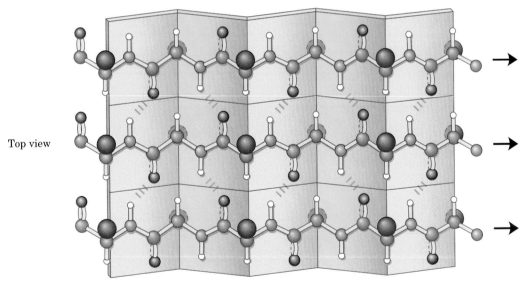

Side view

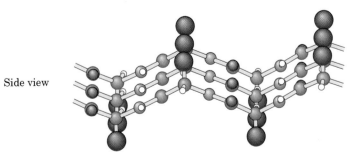

figure 6–7

The β conformation of polypeptide chains. These top and side views reveal the R groups extending out from the β sheet and emphasize the pleated shape described by the planes of the peptide bonds. (An alternate name for this structure is β-pleated sheet.) Hydrogen-bond cross-links between adjacent chains are also shown. **(a)** Antiparallel β sheet, in which the amino-terminal to carboxyl-terminal orientation of adjacent chains (arrows) is inverse. **(b)** Parallel β sheet.

β Turns Are Common in Proteins

In globular proteins, which have a compact folded structure, nearly one-third of the amino acid residues are in turns or loops where the polypeptide chain reverses direction (Fig. 6–8). These are the connecting elements that link successive runs of α helix or β conformation. Particularly common are **β turns** that connect the ends of two adjacent segments of an antiparallel β sheet. The structure is a 180° turn involving four amino acid residues, with the carbonyl oxygen of the first amino acid residue forming a hydrogen bond with the amino-group hydrogen of the fourth. The peptide groups of the central two residues do not participate in any interresidue hydrogen bonding. Gly and Pro residues often occur in β turns, the former because it is small and flexible, the latter because peptide bonds involving the imino nitrogen of proline readily assume the cis configuration (Fig. 6–8b), a form that is particularly amenable to a tight turn. Of the several types of β turns, the two shown in Figure 6–8 are the most common. Beta turns are often found near the surface of a protein, where the peptide groups of the central two amino acid residues in the turn can hydrogen bond with water. Considerably less common is the γ turn, a three-residue turn with a hydrogen bond between the first and third residues.

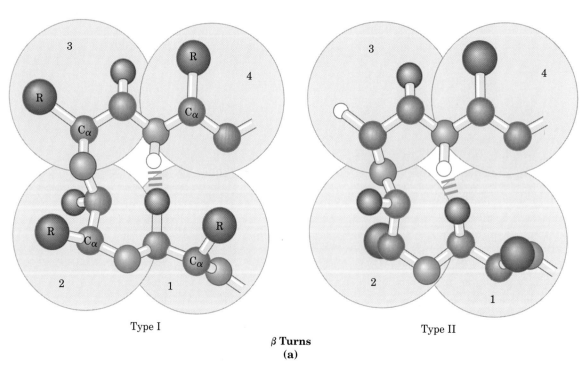

Type I

Type II

β Turns
(a)

figure 6–8
Structures of β turns. (a) Type I and type II β turns are most common; type I turns occur more than twice as frequently as type II. Type II β turns always have Gly as the third residue. Note the hydrogen bond between the peptide groups of the first and fourth residues of the bends. (Individual amino acid residues are framed by large blue circles.) **(b)** The trans and cis isomers of a peptide bond involving the imino nitrogen of proline. Of the peptide bonds between amino acid residues other than Pro, over 99.95% are in the trans configuration. For peptide bonds involving the imino nitrogen of proline, however, about 6% are in the cis configuration; many of these occur at β turns.

trans

cis

Proline isomers
(b)

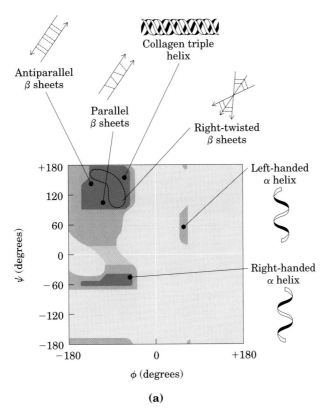

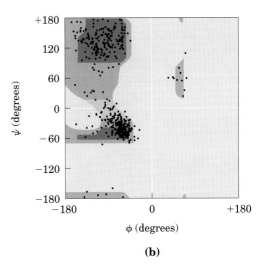

(a)

(b)

figure 6–9

Ramachandran plots for a variety of structures. (a) The values of ϕ and ψ for various allowed secondary structures are overlaid on the plot from Figure 6–3. Although left-handed α helices extending over several amino acid residues are theoretically possible, they have not been observed in proteins. **(b)** The values of ϕ and ψ for all the amino acid residues except Gly in the enzyme pyruvate kinase (isolated from rabbit) are overlaid on the plot of theoretically allowed conformations (Fig. 6–3). The small, flexible Gly residues were excluded because they frequently fall outside the expected ranges (blue). (Data for **(b)** courtesy of Hazel Holden, University of Wisconsin Enzyme Institute.)

Common Secondary Structures Have Characteristic Bond Angles and Amino Acid Content

The α helix and the β conformation are the major repetitive secondary structures in a wide variety of proteins, although other repetitive structures do exist in some specialized proteins (an example is collagen; see Fig. 6–13).

Every type of secondary structure can be completely described by the bond angles ϕ and ψ at each residue. As shown by a Ramachandran plot, the α helix and β conformation fall within a relatively restricted range of sterically allowed structures (Fig. 6–9a). Most values of ϕ and ψ taken from known protein structures fall into the expected regions, with high concentrations near the α helix and β conformation values as predicted (Fig. 6–9b). The only amino acid residue often found in a conformation outside these regions is glycine. Because its side chain, a single hydrogen atom, is small, a Gly residue can take part in many conformations that are sterically forbidden for other amino acids.

Some amino acids are accommodated better than others in the different types of secondary structures. An overall summary is presented in Figure 6–10. Some biases, such as the common presence of Pro and Gly residues in β turns and their relative absence in α helices, is readily explained by the known constraints on the different secondary structures. Other evident biases may be explained by taking into account the sizes or charges of side chains, but not all the trends in Figure 6–10 are understood.

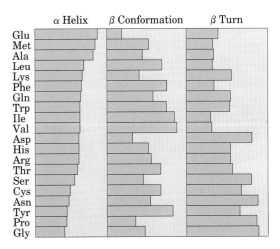

figure 6–10

Relative probabilities that a given amino acid will occur in the three common types of secondary structure.

Protein Tertiary and Quaternary Structures

The overall three-dimensional arrangement of all atoms in a protein is referred to as the protein's **tertiary structure.** Whereas the term secondary structure refers to the spatial arrangement of amino acid residues that are adjacent in the primary structure, tertiary structure includes *longer-range* aspects of amino acid sequence. Amino acids that are far apart in the polypeptide sequence and that reside in different types of secondary structure may interact within the completely folded structure of a protein. The location of bends (including β turns) in the polypeptide chain and the direction and angle of these bends are determined by the number and location of specific bend-producing residues, such as Pro, Thr, Ser, and Gly. Interacting segments of polypeptide chains are held in their characteristic tertiary positions by different kinds of weak-bonding interactions (and sometimes by covalent bonds such as disulfide cross-links) between the segments.

Some proteins contain two or more separate polypeptide chains or subunits, which may be identical or different. The arrangement of these protein subunits in three-dimensional complexes constitutes **quaternary structure.**

In considering these higher levels of structure, it is useful to classify proteins into two major groups: **fibrous proteins,** having polypeptide chains arranged in long strands or sheets, and **globular proteins,** having polypeptide chains folded into a spherical or globular shape. The two groups are structurally distinct: fibrous proteins usually consist largely of a single type of secondary structure; globular proteins often contain several types of secondary structure. The groups differ functionally in that the structures that provide support, shape, and external protection to vertebrates are made of fibrous proteins, whereas most enzymes and regulatory proteins are globular proteins. Certain fibrous proteins played a key role in the development of our modern understanding of protein structure and provide particularly clear examples of the relationship between structure and function. We begin our discussion with fibrous proteins before turning to the more complex folding patterns observed in globular proteins.

Fibrous Proteins Are Adapted for a Structural Function

α-Keratin, collagen, and silk fibroin nicely illustrate the relationship between protein structure and biological function (Table 6–1). Fibrous proteins share properties that give strength and/or flexibility to the structures in which they occur. In each case, the fundamental structural unit is a simple repeating element of secondary structure. All fibrous proteins are insoluble in water, a property conferred by a high concentration of hydrophobic amino acid residues both in the interior of the protein and on its surface. These hydrophobic surfaces are largely buried by packing many similar polypeptide chains together to form elaborate supramolecular complexes.

table 6–1

Secondary Structures and Properties of Fibrous Proteins

Structure	Characteristics	Examples of occurrence
α Helix, cross-linked by disulfide bonds	Tough, insoluble protective structures of varying hardness and flexibility	α-Keratin of hair, feathers, and nails
β Conformation	Soft, flexible filaments	Silk fibroin
Collagen triple helix	High tensile strength, without stretch	Collagen of tendons, bone matrix

The underlying structural simplicity of fibrous proteins makes them particularly useful for illustrating some of the fundamental principles of protein structure discussed above.

α-**Keratin**   The α-keratins have evolved for strength. Found in mammals, these proteins constitute almost the entire dry weight of hair, wool, nails, claws, quills, horns, hooves, and much of the outer layer of skin. The α-keratins are part of a broader family of proteins called intermediate filament (IF) proteins. Other IF proteins are found in the cystoskeletons of animal cells. All IF proteins have a structural function and share structural features exemplified by the α-keratins.

The α-keratin helix is a right-handed α helix, the same helix found in many other proteins. Francis Crick and Linus Pauling in the early 1950s independently suggested that the α helices of keratin were arranged as a coiled coil. Two strands of α-keratin, oriented in parallel (with their amino termini at the same end) are wrapped about each other to form a supertwisted coiled coil. The supertwisting amplifies the strength of the overall structure, just as strands are twisted to make a strong rope (Fig. 6–11). The twisting of the axis of an α helix to form a coiled coil explains the discrepancy between the 5.4 Å per turn predicted for an α helix by Pauling and Corey and the 5.15 to 5.2 Å repeating structure observed in the x-ray diffraction of hair (p. 6-5). The helical path of the supertwists is left-handed, opposite in sense to the α helix. The surfaces where the two α helices touch are made up of hydrophobic amino acid residues, their R groups meshed together in a regular interlocking pattern. This permits a close packing of the polypeptide chains within the left-handed supertwist. Not surprisingly, α-keratin is rich in the hydrophobic residues Ala, Val, Leu, Ile, Met, and Phe.

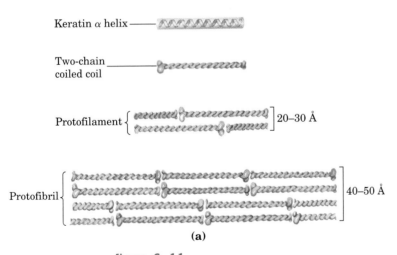

(a)

figure 6–11
Structure of hair. (a) Hair α-keratin is an elongated α helix with somewhat thicker elements near the amino and carboxyl termini. Pairs of these helices are interwound in a left-handed sense to form two-chain coiled coils. These then combine in higher-order structures called protofilaments and protofibrils. About four protofibrils—32 strands of α-keratin altogether—combine to form an intermediate filament. The individual two-chain coiled coils in the various substructures also appear to be interwound, but the handedness of the interwinding and other structural details are unknown. **(b)** A hair is an array of many α-keratin filaments, made up of the substructures shown in **(a)**.

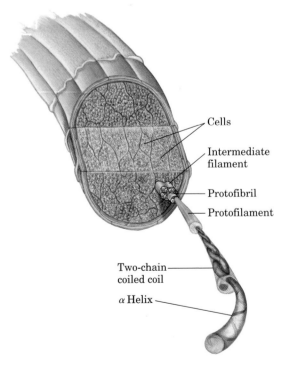

Cross section of a hair
(b)

An individual polypeptide in the α-keratin coiled coil has a relatively simple tertiary structure, dominated by an α-helical secondary structure with its helical axis twisted in a left-handed superhelix. The intertwining of the two α-helical polypeptides is an example of quaternary structure. Coiled coils of this type are common structural elements in filamentous proteins. The quaternary structure of α-keratin can be quite complex. Many coiled coils can be assembled into large supramolecular complexes, such as the arrangement of α-keratin to form the intermediate filament of hair (Fig. 6–11b).

The strength of fibrous proteins is enhanced by covalent cross-links between polypeptide chains within the multihelical "ropes" and between adjacent chains in a supramolecular assembly. In α-keratins, the cross-links stabilizing quaternary structure are disulfide bonds (Box 6–2). In the hardest and toughest α-keratins, such as those of rhinoceros horn, up to 18% of the residues are cysteines involved in disulfide bonds.

---

box 6–2   Permanent Waving Is Biochemical Engineering

When hair is exposed to moist heat, it can be stretched. At the molecular level, the α helices in the α-keratin of hair are stretched out until they arrive at the fully extended β conformation. On cooling they spontaneously revert to the α-helical conformation. The characteristic "stretchability" of α-keratins, as well as their numerous disulfide cross-linkages, are the basis of permanent waving. The hair to be waved or curled is first bent around a form of appropriate shape. A solution of a reducing agent, usually a compound containing a thiol or sulfhydryl group (—SH), is then applied with heat. The reducing agent cleaves the cross-linkages by reducing each disulfide bond to form two Cys residues. The moist heat breaks hydrogen bonds and causes the α-helical structure of the polypeptide chains to uncoil. After a time the reducing solution is removed, and an oxidizing agent is added to establish *new* disulfide bonds between pairs of Cys residues of adjacent polypeptide chains, but not the same pairs as before the treatment. After the hair is washed and cooled, the polypeptide chains revert to their α-helical conformation. The hair fibers now curl in the desired fashion because the new disulfide cross-linkages exert some torsion or twist on the bundles of α-helical coils in the hair fibers. A permanent wave is not truly permanent because the hair grows; in the new hair replacing the old, the α-keratin has the natural, nonwavy pattern of disulfide bonds.

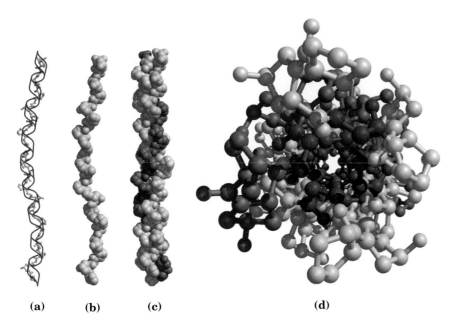

(a)   (b)   (c)   (d)

figure 6–12
Structure of collagen. (a) The α chain of collagen has
a repeating secondary structure unique to this protein.
The repeating tripeptide sequence Gly–X–Pro or
Gly–X–HyPro adopts a left-handed helical structure with
three residues per turn. The repeating sequence used to
generate this model is Gly–Pro–HyPro. **(b)** Space-filling
model of the same α chain. **(c)** Three of these helices
(shown here in gray, light blue, and dark blue) wrap
around one another with a right-handed twist. **(d)** The
three-stranded collagen superhelix shown from one end,
in a ball-and-stick representation. Gly residues are shown
in red. Glycine, because of its small size, is required at
the tight junction where the three chains are in contact.
The balls in this illustration do not represent the van der
Waals radii of the individual atoms. The center of the
three-stranded superhelix is not hollow as it appears here,
but is very tightly packed.

Collagen   Like the α-keratins, collagen has evolved to provide strength. It
is found in connective tissue such as tendons, cartilage, the organic matrix
of bone, and the cornea of the eye. The collagen helix is a unique secondary
structure quite distinct from the α helix. It is left-handed and has three
amino acid residues per turn (Fig. 6–12). Collagen is also a coiled coil, but
one with distinct tertiary and quaternary structure: three separate polypeptides, called α chains (not to be confused with α helices), are supertwisted
about each other (Fig. 6–12c). The superhelical twisting is right-handed in
collagen, opposite in sense to the left-handed helix of the α chains.

Collagen is 35% Gly, 11% Ala, and 21% Pro and HyPro (hydroxyproline,
a nonstandard amino acid). The food product gelatin, derived from collagen, has little nutritional value as a protein because collagen is extremely
low in many amino acids that are essential in the human diet. The unusual
amino acid content of collagen is related to structural constraints unique to
the collagen helix. The amino acid sequence in collagen is generally a repeating tripeptide unit, Gly–X–Pro or Gly–X–HyPro, where X can be any
amino acid residue. Only Gly residues can be accommodated at the very
tight junctions between the individual α chains (Fig. 6–12d); Pro residues
permit the sharp twisting of the collagen helix. The amino acid sequence
and the supertwisted quaternary structure of collagen allow a very close
packing of its three polypeptides.

The tight wrapping of the α chains in the collagen triple helix provides
tensile strength greater than that of a steel wire of equal cross section. Collagen fibrils (Fig. 6–13) are supramolecular assemblies consisting of triple-

figure 6–13
Structure of collagen fibrils. Collagen (M_r 300,000) is a
rod-shaped molecule, about 3,000 Å long and only 15 Å
thick. Its three helically intertwined α chains may have
different sequences, but each has about 1,000 amino
acid residues. Collagen fibrils are made up of collagen
molecules aligned in a staggered fashion and cross-linked
for strength. The specific alignment and degree of cross-
linking vary with the tissue and produce characteristic
cross-striations in an electron micrograph. In the example
shown here, alignment of the head groups of every fourth
molecule produces striations 640 Å apart.

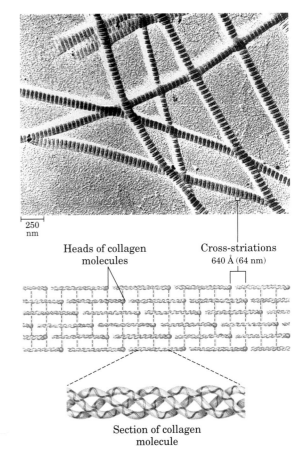

250
nm

Heads of collagen   Cross-striations
molecules   640 Å (64 nm)

Section of collagen
molecule

helical collagen molecules (sometimes referred to as tropocollagen mole-cules) associated in a variety of ways to provide different degrees of tensile strength. The α chains of collagen molecules and the collagen molecules of fibrils are cross-linked by unusual types of covalent bonds involving Lys, HyLys (hydroxylysine), or His residues. These links create nonstandard amino acid residues such as dehydrohydroxylysinonorleucine. The increas-ingly rigid and brittle character of connective tissue as people age results from an accumulation of covalent cross-links in collagen fibrils.

$$
\begin{array}{c}
\text{H—N} \\
\qquad \text{CH—CH}_2\text{—CH}_2\text{—CH}_2\text{—CH=N—CH}_2\text{—CH—CH}_2\text{—CH}_2\text{—CH} \\
\text{O=C} \qquad\qquad\qquad\qquad\qquad\qquad\qquad \text{OH} \qquad\qquad \text{C=O}
\end{array}
$$

| Polypeptide chain | Lys residue minus ε-amino group (norleucine) | HyLys residue | Polypeptide chain |

Dehydrohydroxylysinonorleucine

A typical mammal has more than 30 different structural variants of col-lagen that occur in particular tissues. Each is somewhat different in se-quence and function. Some human genetic defects in collagen structure illustrate the close relationship between amino acid sequence and three-dimensional structure in this protein. Osteogenesis imperfecta is characterized by abnormal bone formation in babies; Ehlers-Danlos syn-drome by loose joints. Both conditions can be lethal, and both result from the substitution of an amino acid residue with a larger R group (such as Cys or Ser) for a single Gly residue in each α chain (a different Gly residue in each disorder). These single-residue substitutions have a catastrophic ef-fect on collagen function because they disrupt the Gly–X–Pro repeat that gives collagen its unique helical structure. Given its role in the collagen triple helix (Fig. 6–12d), Gly cannot be replaced by another amino acid residue without substantial deleterious effects on the structure.

Silk Fibroin Fibroin, the protein of silk, is produced by insects and spiders. Its polypeptide chains are predominantly in the β conformation. Fibroin is rich in Ala and Gly residues, permitting a close packing of β sheets and an interlocking arrangement of R groups (Fig. 6–14). The overall structure is

figure 6–14

Structure of silk. The fibers used to make silk cloth or a spider web are made up of the protein fibroin. **(a)** Fibroin consists of layers of antiparallel β sheets rich in Ala (purple) and Gly (yellow) residues. The small side chains interdigitate and allow close packing of each layered sheet, as shown in this side view. **(b)** Strands of fibroin (blue) emerge from the spinnerets of a spider in this colorized electron micrograph.

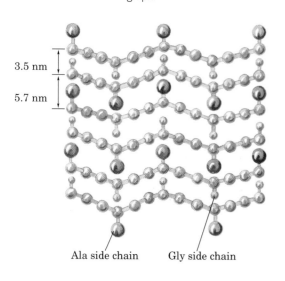

3.5 nm

5.7 nm

Ala side chain   Gly side chain

(a)

70 μm

(b)

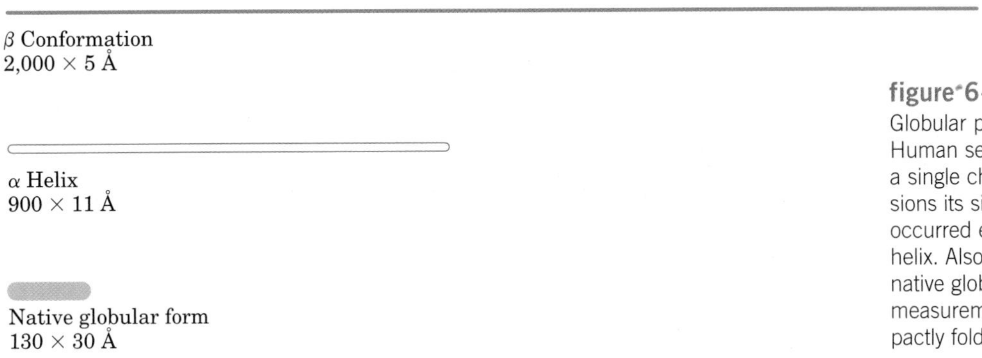

β Conformation
2,000 × 5 Å

α Helix
900 × 11 Å

Native globular form
130 × 30 Å

figure 6–15
Globular protein structures are compact and varied. Human serum albumin (M_r 64,500) has 585 residues in a single chain. Given here are the approximate dimensions its single polypeptide chain would have if it occurred entirely in extended β conformation or as an α helix. Also shown is the actual size of the protein in its native globular form, as determined by physicochemical measurements; the polypeptide chain must be very compactly folded to fit into these dimensions.

stabilized by extensive hydrogen bonding between all peptide linkages in the polypeptides of each β sheet and by the optimization of van der Waals interactions between sheets. Silk does not stretch because the β conformation is already highly extended (Fig. 6–7; see also Fig. 6–15). However, the structure is flexible because the sheets are held together by numerous weak interactions rather than by covalent bonds such as the disulfide bonds in α-keratins.

Structural Diversity Reflects Functional Diversity in Globular Proteins

In a globular protein, different segments of a polypeptide chain (or multiple polypeptide chains) fold back on each other. As illustrated in Figure 6–15, this folding generates a compact form relative to polypeptides in a fully extended conformation. The folding also provides the structural diversity necessary for proteins to carry out a wide array of biological functions. Globular proteins include enzymes, transport proteins, motor proteins, regulatory proteins, immunoglobulins, and proteins with many other functions.

As a new millenium begins, the number of known three-dimensional protein structures is in the thousands and more than doubles every two years. This wealth of structural information is revolutionizing our understanding of protein structure, the relation of structure to function, and even the evolutionary paths by which proteins arrived at their present state, which can be glimpsed in the family resemblances among proteins that are revealed as protein databases are sifted and sorted. The sheer variety of structures can seem daunting, yet as new protein structures become available it is becoming increasingly clear that they are manifestations of a finite set of recognizable, stable folding patterns.

Our discussion of globular protein structure begins with the principles gleaned from the earliest protein structures to be elucidated. This is followed by a detailed description of protein substructure and comparative categorization. Such discussions are only possible because of the vast amount of information available over the Internet from resources such as the Protein Data Bank (PDB), an archive of experimentally determined three-dimensional structures of biological macromolecules.

Myoglobin Provided Early Clues about the Complexity of Globular Protein Structure

The first breakthrough in understanding the three-dimensional structure of a globular protein came from x-ray diffraction studies of myoglobin carried out by John Kendrew and his colleagues in the 1950s. Myoglobin is a relatively small (M_r 16,700), oxygen-binding protein of muscle cells. It functions both to store oxygen and to facilitate oxygen diffusion in rapidly contracting muscle tissue. Myoglobin contains a single polypeptide chain of 153 amino acid residues of known sequence and a single iron protoporphyrin, or

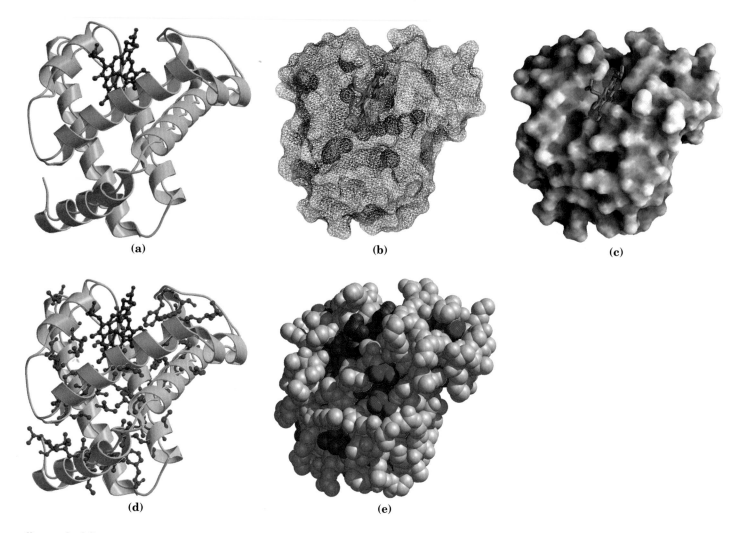

(a)   (b)   (c)

(d)   (e)

figure 6–16

Tertiary structure of sperm whale myoglobin. The orientation of the protein is similar in all panels; the heme group is shown in red. In addition to illustrating the myoglobin structure, this figure provides examples of several different ways to display protein structure. **(a)** The polypeptide backbone, shown in a ribbon representation of a type introduced by Jane Richardson, which highlights regions of secondary structure. The α-helical regions are evident. **(b)** A "mesh" image emphasizes the protein surface. **(c)** A surface contour image is useful for visualizing pockets in the protein where other molecules might bind. **(d)** A ribbon representation, including side chains (blue) for the hydrophobic residues Leu, Ile, Val, and Phe. **(e)** A space-filling model with all amino acid side chains. Each atom is represented by a sphere encompassing its van der Waals radius. The hydrophobic residues are again shown in blue; most are not visible because they are buried in the interior of the protein.

heme, group. The same heme group is found in hemoglobin, the oxygen-binding protein of erythrocytes, and is responsible for the deep red-brown color of both myoglobin and hemoglobin. Myoglobin is particularly abundant in the muscles of diving mammals such as the whale, seal, and porpoise, whose muscles are so rich in this protein that they are brown. Storage and distribution of oxygen by muscle myoglobin permits these animals to remain submerged for long periods of time.

Figure 6–16 shows several structural representations of myoglobin, illustrating how the polypeptide chain is folded in three dimensions—its tertiary structure. The red group surrounded by protein is heme. The backbone of the myoglobin molecule is made up of eight relatively straight segments of α helix interrupted by bends, some of which are β turns. The longest α helix has 23 amino acid residues and the shortest only seven; all are right-handed. More than 70% of the amino acid residues in myoglobin are in these α-helical regions. X-ray analysis has revealed the precise position of each of the R groups, which occupy nearly all the space within the folded chain.

Many important conclusions were drawn from the structure of myoglobin. The positioning of amino acid side chains reflects a structure that derives much of its stability from hydrophobic interactions. Most of the hydrophobic R groups are in the interior of the myoglobin molecule, hidden from exposure to water. All but two of the polar R groups are located on the outer surface of the molecule, and all are hydrated. The myoglobin molecule is so compact that its interior has room for only four molecules of

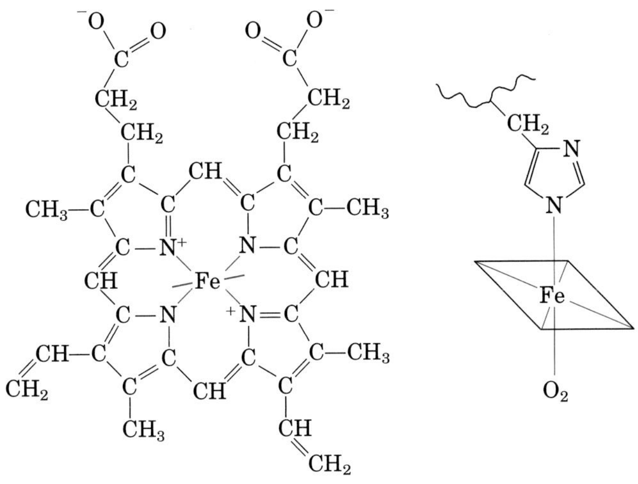

figure 6–17
The heme group. This group is present in myoglobin, hemoglobin, cytochromes, and many other heme proteins. **(a)** Heme consists of a complex organic ring structure, protoporphyrin, to which is bound an iron atom in its ferrous (Fe^{2+}) state. The iron atom has six coordination bonds, four in the plane of, and bonded to, the flat porphyrin molecule and two perpendicular to it. **(b)** In myoglobin and hemoglobin, one of the perpendicular coordination bonds is bound to a nitrogen atom of a His residue. The other is "open" and serves as the binding site for an O_2 molecule.

water. This dense hydrophobic core is typical of globular proteins. The fraction of space occupied by atoms in an organic liquid is 0.4 to 0.6; in a typical crystal the fraction is 0.70 to 0.78, near the theoretical maximum. In a globular protein the fraction is about 0.75, comparable to that in a crystal. In this closely packed environment, weak interactions strengthen and reinforce each other. For example, the nonpolar side chains in the core are so close together that short-range van der Waals interactions make a significant contribution to stabilizing hydrophobic interactions.

Deduction of the structure of myoglobin confirmed some expectations and introduced some new elements of secondary structure. As predicted by Pauling and Corey, all the peptide bonds are in the planar trans configuration. The α helices in myoglobin provided the first direct experimental evidence for the existence of this type of secondary structure. Each of the four Pro residues of myoglobin occurs at a bend (recall that proline, with its fixed ϕ bond angle and lack of a peptide-bond N—H group for participation in hydrogen bonds, is largely incompatible with α-helical structure). Other bends contain Ser, Thr, and Asn residues, which are among the amino acids whose bulk and shape tend to make them incompatible with α-helical structure if they are in close proximity in the amino acid sequence (p. 6-7).

The flat heme group rests in a crevice, or pocket, in the myoglobin molecule. The iron atom in the center of the heme group has two bonding (coordination) positions perpendicular to the plane of the heme (Fig. 6–17). One of these is bound to the R group of the His residue at position 93; the other is the site at which an O_2 molecule binds. Within this pocket, the accessibility of the heme group to solvent is highly restricted. This is important for function because free heme groups in an oxygenated solution are rapidly oxidized from the ferrous (Fe^{2+}) form, which is active in the reversible binding of O_2, to the ferric (Fe^{3+}) form, which does not bind O_2.

Knowledge of the structure of myoglobin allowed researchers for the first time to understand in detail the correlation between the structure and function of a protein. Hundreds of proteins have been subjected to similar analysis since then. Today, techniques such as NMR spectroscopy supplement x-ray diffraction data, providing more information on a protein's structure (Box 6–3). The ongoing sequencing of genomic DNA from many organisms has identified thousands of genes that encode proteins of known sequence but unknown function. Our first insight into what these proteins do often comes from our still-limited understanding of how primary structure determines tertiary structure, and how tertiary structure determines function.

X-Ray Diffraction

The spacing of atoms in a crystal lattice can be determined by measuring the locations and intensities of spots produced on photographic film by a beam of x rays of given wavelength, after the beam has been diffracted by the electrons of the atoms. For example, x-ray analysis of sodium chloride crystals shows that Na^+ and Cl^- ions are arranged in a simple cubic lattice. The spacing of the different kinds of atoms in complex organic molecules, even very large ones such as proteins, can also be analyzed by x-ray diffraction methods. However, the technique for analyzing crystals of complex molecules is far more laborious than for simple salt crystals. When the repeating pattern of the crystal is a molecule as large as, say, a protein, the numerous atoms in the molecule yield thousands of diffraction spots that must be analyzed by computer.

The process may be understood at an elementary level by considering how images are generated in a light microscope. Light from a point source is focused on an object. The light waves are scattered by the object, and these scattered waves are recombined by a series of lenses to generate an enlarged image of the object. The smallest object whose structure can be determined by such a system (i.e., the resolving power of the microscope) is determined by the wavelength of the light—in this case, visible light, with wavelengths in the range of 400 to 700 nm. Objects smaller than half the wavelength of the incident light cannot be resolved. To resolve objects as small as proteins we must use x rays, with wavelengths in the range of 0.7 to 1.5 Å (0.07 to 0.15 nm). However, there are no lenses that can recombine x rays to form an image; instead the pattern of diffracted x rays is collected directly and an image is reconstructed by mathematical techniques.

The amount of information obtained from x-ray crystallography depends on the degree of structural order in the sample. Some important structural parameters were obtained from early studies of the diffraction patterns of the fibrous proteins arranged in fairly regular arrays in hair and wool. However, the orderly bundles formed by fibrous proteins are not crystals—the molecules are aligned side by side, but not all are oriented in the same direction. More detailed three-dimensional structural information about proteins requires a highly ordered protein crystal. Protein crystallization is something of an empirical science, and the structures of many important proteins are not yet known simply because they have proved difficult to crystallize. Practitioners have compared making protein crystals to holding together a stack of bowling balls with cellophane tape.

Operationally, there are several steps in x-ray

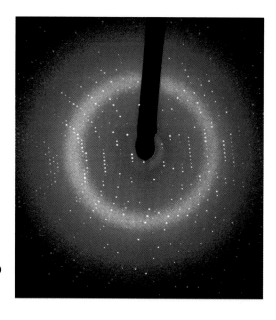

(a)

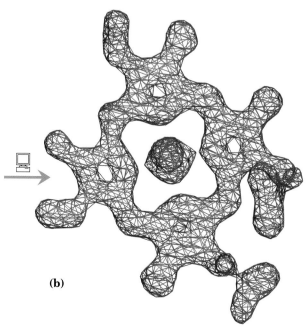

(b)

structural analysis (Fig. 1). Once a crystal is obtained, it is placed in an x-ray beam between the x-ray source and a detector, and a regular array of spots called reflections is generated. The spots are created by the diffracted x-ray beam, and each atom in a molecule makes a contribution to each spot. An electron-density map of the protein is reconstructed from the overall diffraction pattern of spots by using a mathematical technique called a Fourier transform. In effect, the computer acts as a "computational lens." A model for the structure is then built that is consistent with the electron-density map.

John Kendrew found that the x-ray diffraction pattern of crystalline myoglobin (isolated from muscles of the sperm whale) is very complex, with nearly 25,000 reflections. Computer analysis of these reflections took place in stages. The resolution improved at each stage, until in 1959 the positions of virtually all the non-hydrogen atoms in the protein had been determined. The amino acid sequence of the protein, obtained by chemical analysis, was consistent with the molecular model. The structures of thousands of proteins, many of them much more complex than myoglobin, have since been determined to a similar level of resolution.

The physical environment within a crystal is not identical to that in solution or in a living cell. A crystal imposes a space and time average on the structure deduced from its analysis, and x-ray diffraction studies provide little information about molecular motion within the protein. The conformation of proteins in a crystal could in principle also be affected by nonphysiological factors such as incidental protein-protein contacts within the crystal. However, when structures derived from the analysis of crystals are compared with structural information obtained by other means (such as NMR, as described below), the crystal-derived structure almost always represents a functional conformation of the protein. X-ray crystallography can be applied successfully to proteins too large to be structurally analyzed by NMR.

figure 1

Steps in the determination of the structure of sperm whale myoglobin by x-ray crystallography. **(a)** X-ray diffraction patterns are generated from a crystal of the protein. **(b)** Data extracted from the diffraction patterns are used to calculate a three-dimensional electron-density map of the protein. The electron density of only part of the structure, the heme, is shown. **(c)** Regions of greatest electron density reveal the location of atomic nuclei, and this information is used to piece together the final structure. Here, the heme structure is modeled into its electron density map. **(d)** The completed structure of sperm whale myoglobin, including the heme.

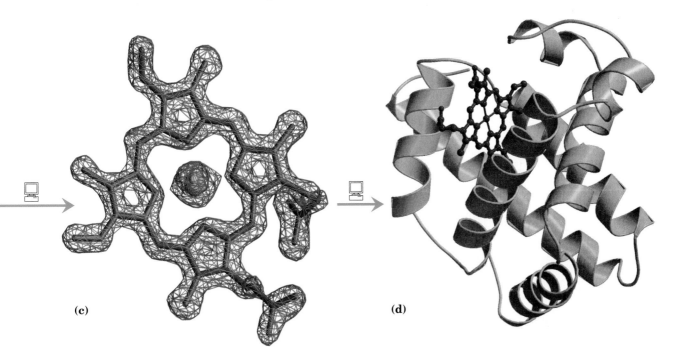

(c)   (d)

Continued on next page

Nuclear Magnetic Resonance

An important complementary method for determining the three-dimensional structures of macromolecules is nuclear magnetic resonance (NMR). Modern NMR techniques are being used to determine the structures of ever-larger macromolecules, including carbohydrates, nucleic acids, and small to average-sized proteins. An advantage of NMR studies is that they are carried out on macromolecules in solution, whereas x-ray crystallography is limited to molecules that can be crystallized. NMR can also illuminate the dynamic side of protein structure, including conformational changes, protein folding, and interactions with other molecules.

NMR is a manifestation of nuclear spin angular momentum, a quantum mechanical property of atomic nuclei. Only certain atoms, including ^{1}H, ^{13}C, ^{15}N, ^{19}F, and ^{31}P, possess the kind of nuclear spin that gives rise to an NMR signal. Nuclear spin generates a magnetic dipole. When a strong, static magnetic field is applied to a solution containing a single type of macromolecule, the magnetic dipoles are aligned in the field in one of two orientations, parallel (low energy) or antiparallel (high energy). A short ($\sim$10 μs) pulse of electromagnetic energy of suitable frequency (the resonant frequency, which is in the radio frequency range) is applied at right angles to the nuclei aligned in the magnetic field. Some energy is absorbed as nuclei switch to the high-energy state, and the absorption spectrum that results contains information about the identity of the nuclei and their immediate chemical environment. The data from many such experiments performed on a sample are averaged, increasing the signal-to-noise ratio, and an NMR spectrum such as that in Figure 2 is generated.

^{1}H is particularly important in NMR experiments because of its high sensitivity and natural abundance. For macromolecules, ^{1}H NMR spectra can become quite complicated. Even a small protein has hundreds of ^{1}H atoms, typically resulting in a one-dimensional NMR spectrum too complex for analysis. Structural analysis of proteins became possible with the advent of two-dimensional NMR techniques (Fig. 3). These methods allow measurement of distance-dependent coupling of nuclear spins in nearby atoms through space (the nuclear Overhauser effect (NOE), in a method dubbed NOESY) or the coupling of nuclear spins in atoms connected by covalent bonds (total correlation spectroscopy, or TOCSY).

Translating a two-dimensional NMR spectrum into a complete three-dimensional structure can be a laborious process. The NOE signals provide some information about the distances between individual atoms, but for these distance constraints to be useful, the atoms giving rise to each signal must be identified. Complementary TOCSY experiments can help identify which NOE signals reflect atoms that are linked by covalent bonds. Certain patterns of NOE signals have been associated with secondary structures such as α helices. Modern genetic engineering can be used to prepare proteins that contain the rare isotopes ^{13}C or ^{15}N. The new NMR signals produced by these atoms, and the coupling with ^{1}H signals resulting from these substitutions, help in the assignment of individual ^{1}H NOE signals. The process is also aided by a knowledge of the amino acid sequence of the polypeptide.

To generate a three-dimensional structure, the distance constraints are fed into a computer along with known geometric constraints such as chirality, van der Waals radii, and bond lengths and angles. The computer generates a family of closely related structures that represent the

figure 2
A one-dimensional NMR spectrum of a globin from a marine blood worm. This protein and sperm whale myoglobin are very close structural analogs, belonging to the same protein structural family and sharing an oxygen-transport function.

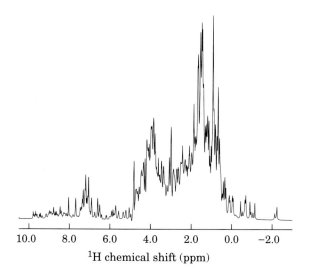

^{1}H chemical shift (ppm)

(a)

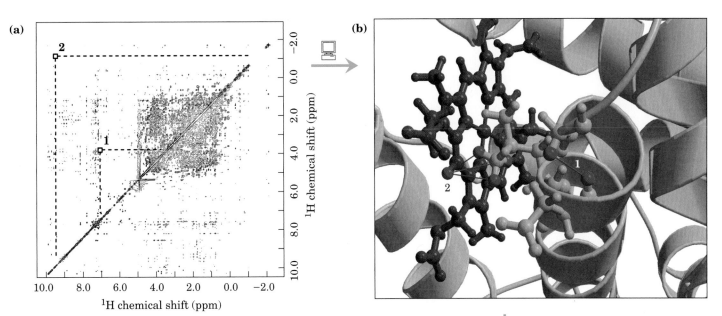

(b)

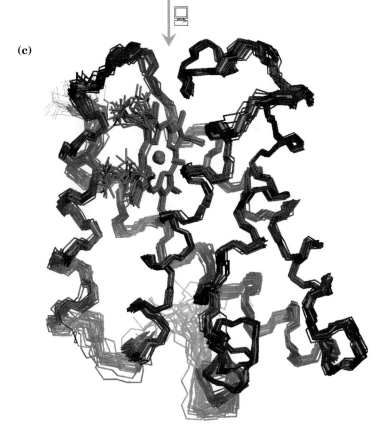

(c)

figure 3

The use of two-dimensional NMR to generate a three-dimensional structure of a globin, the same protein used to generate the data in Figure 2. The diagonal in a two-dimensional NMR spectrum is equivalent to a one-dimensional spectrum. The off-diagonal peaks are NOE signals generated by close-range interactions of ^1H atoms that may generate signals quite distant in the one-dimensional spectrum. Two such interactions are identified in **(a),** and their identities are shown with blue lines in **(b).** Three lines are drawn for interaction 2 between a methyl group in the protein and a hydrogen on the heme. The methyl group rotates rapidly such that each of its three hydrogens contributes equally to the interaction and the NMR signal. Such information is used to determine the complete three-dimensional structure, as in **(c).** The multiple lines shown for the protein backbone represent the family of structures consistent with the distance constraints in the NMR data. The structural similarity with myoglobin (see Fig. 1) is evident. The proteins are oriented in the same way in both figures.

range of conformations consistent with the NOE distance constraints (Fig. 3c). The uncertainty in structures generated by NMR is in part a reflection of the molecular vibrations (breathing) within a protein structure in solution, discussed in more detail in Chapter 7. Normal experimental uncertainty can also play a role.

When a protein structure has been determined by both x-ray crystallography and NMR, the structures generally agree well. In some cases, the precise locations of particular amino acid side chains on the protein exterior are different, often because of effects related to the packing of adjacent protein molecules in a crystal. The two techniques together are at the heart of the rapid increase in the availability of structural information about the macromolecules of living cells.

Globular Proteins Have a Variety of Tertiary Structures

With elucidation of the tertiary structures of hundreds of other globular proteins by x-ray analysis, it became clear that myoglobin represents only one of many ways in which a polypeptide chain can be folded. In Figure 6–18 the structures of cytochrome c, lysozyme, and ribonuclease are compared. All have different amino acid sequences and different tertiary structures, reflecting differences in function. All are relatively small and easy to work with, facilitating structural analysis. Cytochrome c is a component of the respiratory chain of mitochondria. Like myoglobin, cytochrome c is a heme protein. It contains a single polypeptide chain of about 100 residues (M_r 12,400) and a single heme group. In this case, the protoporphyrin of the heme group is covalently attached to the polypeptide. Only about 40% of the polypeptide is in α-helical segments, compared with 70% of the myoglobin chain. The rest of the cytochrome c chain contains β turns and irregularly coiled and extended segments.

Lysozyme (M_r 14,600) is an enzyme abundant in egg white and human tears that catalyzes the hydrolytic cleavage of polysaccharides in the protective cell walls of some families of bacteria. Lysozyme, because it can lyse, or degrade, bacterial cell walls, serves as a bactericidal agent. As in cytochrome c, about 40% of its 129 amino acid residues are in α-helical segments, but the arrangement is different and some β-sheet structure is also present (Fig. 6–18). Four disulfide bonds contribute stability to this structure. The α helices line a long crevice in the side of the molecule, called the active site, which is the site of substrate binding and catalysis. The bacterial polysaccharide that is the substrate for lysozyme fits into this crevice.

Ribonuclease, another small globular protein (M_r 13,700), is an enzyme secreted by the pancreas into the small intestine, where it catalyzes the hydrolysis of certain bonds in the ribonucleic acids present in ingested food. Its tertiary structure, determined by x-ray analysis, shows that little of its

figure 6–18

Three-dimensional structures of some small proteins. Shown here are cytochrome c, lysozyme, and ribonuclease. Key functional groups (the heme in cytochrome c; amino acid side chains in the active site of lysozyme and ribonuclease) are shown in red. Disulfide bonds are shown in yellow. Each protein is shown in surface contour and in a ribbon representation, in the same orientation. In the ribbon depictions, regions in the β conformation are represented by flat arrows and the α helices are represented by spiral ribbons.

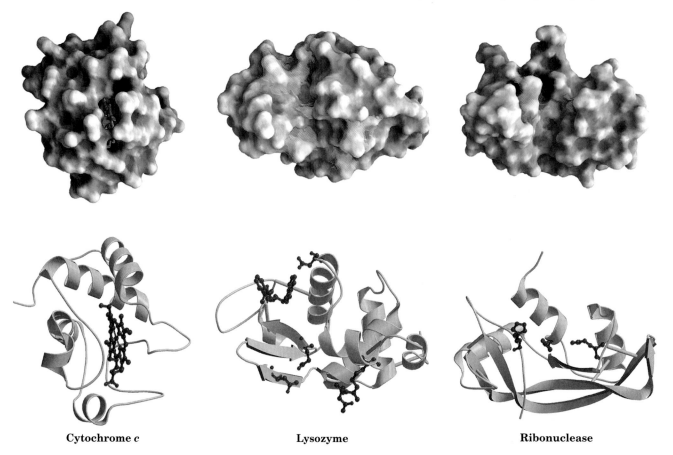

Cytochrome c **Lysozyme**   **Ribonuclease**

table 6–2

Approximate Amounts of α Helix and β Conformation in Some Single-Chain Proteins*

Protein (total residues)	Residues (%)	
	α Helix	β Conformation
Chymotrypsin (247)	14	45
Ribonuclease (124)	26	35
Carboxypeptidase (307)	38	17
Cytochrome c (104)	39	0
Lysozyme (129)	40	12
Myoglobin (153)	78	0

Source: Data from Cantor, C.R. & Schimmel, P.R. (1980) *Biophysical Chemistry,* Part I: *The Conformation of Biological Macromolecules,* p. 100, W.H. Freeman and Company, New York.

*Portions of the polypeptide chains that are not accounted for by α helix or β conformation consist of bends and irregularly coiled or extended stretches. Segments of α helix and β conformation sometimes deviate slightly from their normal dimensions and geometry.

124 amino acid polypeptide chain is in an α-helical conformation, but it contains many segments in the β conformation (Fig. 6–18). Like lysozyme, ribonuclease has four disulfide bonds between loops of the polypeptide chain.

In small proteins, hydrophobic residues are less likely to be sheltered in a hydrophobic interior—simple geometry dictates that the smaller the protein, the lower the ratio of volume to surface area. Small proteins also have fewer potential weak interactions available to stabilize them. This explains why many smaller proteins such as those in Figure 6–18 are stabilized by a number of covalent bonds. Lysozyme and ribonuclease, for example, have disulfide linkages, and the heme group in cytochrome c is covalently linked to the protein on two sides, providing significant stabilization of the entire protein structure.

Table 6–2 shows the proportions of α helix and β conformation (expressed as percentage of residues in each secondary structure) in several small, single-chain, globular proteins. Each of these proteins has a distinct structure, adapted for its particular biological function, but together they share several important properties. Each is folded compactly, and in each case the hydrophobic amino acid side chains are oriented toward the interior (away from water) and the hydrophilic side chains are on the surface. The structures are also stabilized by a multitude of hydrogen bonds and some ionic interactions.

Analysis of Many Globular Proteins Reveals Common Structural Patterns

For the beginning student, the very complex tertiary structures of globular proteins much larger than those shown in Figure 6–18 are best approached by focusing on structural patterns that recur in different and often unrelated proteins. The three-dimensional structure of a typical globular protein can be considered an assemblage of polypeptide segments in the α-helix and β-sheet conformations, linked by connecting segments. The structure can then be described to a first approximation by defining how these segments stack on one another, and how the segments that connect them are arranged. This formalism has led to the development of databases that allow informative comparisons of protein structures, complementing other databases that permit comparisons of protein sequences.

An understanding of a complete three-dimensional structure is built upon an analysis of its parts. We begin by defining terms used to describe protein substructures, then turn to the folding rules elucidated from analysis of the structures of many proteins.

Supersecondary structures, also called **motifs** or simply **folds,** are particularly stable arrangements of several elements of secondary structure and the connections between them. There is no universal agreement among

figure 6–19
Structural domains in the polypeptide troponin C. This calcium-binding protein associated with muscle has separate calcium-binding domains, indicated in blue and purple.

biochemists on the application of the three terms, and they are often used interchangeably. The terms are also applied to a wide range of structures. Recognized motifs range from simple to complex, sometimes appearing in repeating units or combinations. A single large motif may comprise the entire protein. We have already encountered one well-studied motif, the coiled coil of α-keratin, also found in a number of other proteins.

Polypeptides with more than a few hundred amino acid residues often fold into two or more stable, globular units called **domains.** In many cases, a domain from a large protein will retain its correct three-dimensional structure even when it is separated (for example, by proteolytic cleavage) from the remainder of the polypeptide chain. A protein with multiple domains may appear to have a distinct globular lobe for each domain (Fig. 6–19), but, more commonly, extensive contacts between domains make individual domains hard to discern. Different domains often have distinct functions, such as the binding of small molecules or interaction with other proteins. Small proteins usually have only one domain (the domain *is* the protein).

Folding of polypeptides is subject to an array of physical and chemical constraints. A sampling of the prominent folding rules that have emerged provides an opportunity to introduce some simple motifs.

1. Hydrophobic interactions make a large contribution to the stability of protein structures. Burial of hydrophobic amino acid R groups so as to exclude water requires at least two layers of secondary structure. Two simple motifs, the **β-α-β loop** and the **α-α corner** (Fig. 6–20a), create two layers.
2. Where they occur together in proteins, α helices and β sheets generally are found in different structural layers. This is because the backbone of a polypeptide segment in the β conformation (Fig. 6–7) cannot readily hydrogen bond to an α helix aligned with it.
3. Polypeptide segments adjacent to each other in the primary sequence are usually stacked adjacent to each other in the folded structure. Although distant segments of a polypeptide may come together in the tertiary structure, this is not the norm.
4. Connections between elements of secondary structure cannot cross or form knots (Fig. 6–20b).
5. The β conformation is most stable when the individual segments are twisted slightly in a right-handed sense. This influences both the arrangement of β sheets relative to one another and the path of the polypeptide connection between them. Two parallel β strands, for example, must be connected by a crossover strand (Fig. 6–20c). In principle, this crossover could have a right- or left-handed conformation, but in proteins it is almost always in the right-handed form. Right-handed connections tend to be shorter than left-handed connections and to bend through smaller angles, making them easier to form. The twisting of β sheets also leads to a characteristic twisting of the structure formed when many segments are put together. Two examples of resulting structures are the β barrel and twisted β sheet (Fig. 6–20d), which form the core of many larger structures.

Following these rules, complex motifs can be built up from simple ones. For example, a series of β-α-β loops, arranged so that the β strands form a barrel, creates a particularly stable and common motif called the **α/β barrel** (Fig. 6–21). In this structure, each parallel β segment is attached to its neighbor by an α-helical segment. All connections are right-handed. The α/β barrel is found in many enzymes, often with a binding site for a cofactor or substrate in the form of a pocket near one end of the barrel. Note that domains exhibiting similar folding patterns are said to have the same motif even though their constituent α helices and β sheets may differ in length.

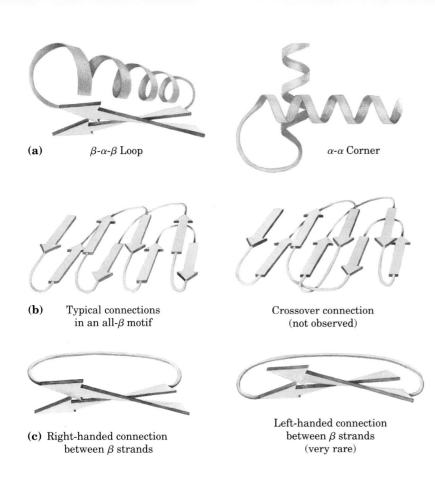

(a) β-α-β Loop

α-α Corner

(b) Typical connections in an all-β motif

Crossover connection (not observed)

(c) Right-handed connection between β strands

Left-handed connection between β strands (very rare)

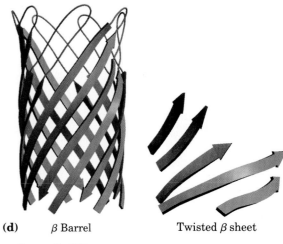

(d) β Barrel

Twisted β sheet

figure 6–20

Stable folding patterns in proteins. **(a)** Two simple and common motifs that provide two layers of secondary structure. Amino acid side chains at the interface between elements of secondary structure are shielded from water. Note that the β strands in the β-α-β loop tend to twist in a right-handed fashion. **(b)** Connections between β strands in layered β sheets. The strands are shown from one end, with no twisting included in the schematic. Thick connections are those at the ends nearest the viewer; thin connections are at the far ends of the β strands. The connections on a given end (e.g., near the viewer) do not cross each other. **(c)** Because of the twist in β strands, connections between strands are generally right-handed. Left-handed connections must traverse sharper angles and are harder to form. **(d)** Two arrangements of β strands stabilized by the tendency of the strands to twist. This β barrel is a single domain of α-hemolysin from the bacterium *Staphylococcus aureus*. The twisted β sheet is from a domain of photolyase from *E. coli*.

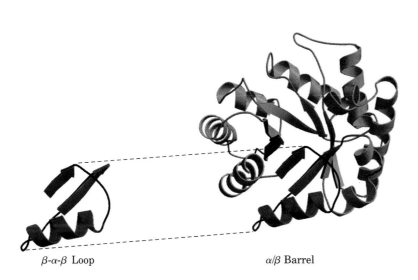

β-α-β Loop

α/β Barrel

figure 6–21

Constructing large motifs from smaller ones. The α/β barrel is a common motif constructed from repetitions of the simpler β-α-β loop motif. This α/β barrel is a domain of the enzyme pyruvate kinase from rabbit.

Protein Motifs Are the Basis for Protein Structural Classification

As we have seen, the complexities of tertiary structure are decreased by considering substructures. Taking this idea further, researchers have organized the complete contents of databases according to hierarchical levels of structure. The Structural Classification of Proteins (SCOP) database offers a good example of this very important trend in biochemistry. At the highest level of classification, the SCOP database borrows a scheme already in common use, in which protein structures are divided into four classes: all α, all β, α/β (in which the α and β segments are interspersed or alternate), and $\alpha + \beta$ (in which the α and β regions are somewhat segregated) (Fig. 6–22).

All α

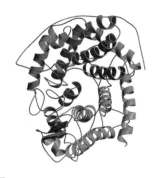

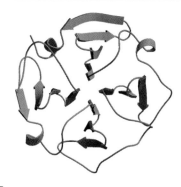

la06
Serum albumin
Serum albumin
Serum albumin
Serum albumin
Human (*Homo sapiens*)

1bcf
Ferritin-like
Ferritin-like
Ferritin
Bacterioferritin (cytochrome b_1)
Escherichia coli

1gai
α/α toroid
Glycosyltransferases of the
    superhelical fold
Glucoamylase
Glucoamylase
Aspergillus awamori, variant x100

1enh
DNA-binding 3-helical bundle
Homeodomain-like
Homeodomain
engrailed Homeodomain
Drosophila melanogaster

All β

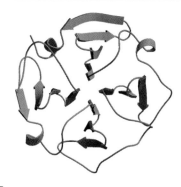

1hoe
α-Amylase inhibitor
α-Amylase inhibitor
α-Amylase inhibitor
HOE-467A
Streptomyces tendae 4158

1lxe
Single-stranded left-handed β helix
Trimeric LpxA-like enzymes
UDP *N*-acetylglucosamine acyltransferase
UDP *N*-acetylglucosamine acyltransferase
Escherichia coli

1pex
Four-bladed β propeller
Hemopexin-like domain
Hemopexin-like domain
Collagenase-3 (MMP-13),
    carboxyl-terminal domain
Human (*Homo sapiens*)

1jpc
β-Prism II
α-D-Mannose-specific plant lectins
α-D-Mannose-specific plant lectins
Lectin (agglutinin)
Snowdrop (*Galanthus nivalis*)

1cd8
Immunoglobulin-like β sandwich
Immunoglobulin
Antibody variable domain-like
CD8
Human (*Homo sapiens*)

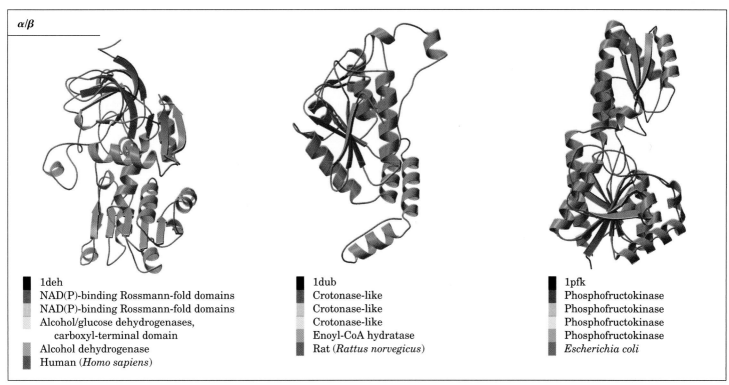

1deh
NAD(P)-binding Rossmann-fold domains
NAD(P)-binding Rossmann-fold domains
Alcohol/glucose dehydrogenases,
  carboxyl-terminal domain
Alcohol dehydrogenase
Human (*Homo sapiens*)

1dub
Crotonase-like
Crotonase-like
Crotonase-like
Enoyl-CoA hydratase
Rat (*Rattus norvegicus*)

1pfk
Phosphofructokinase
Phosphofructokinase
Phosphofructokinase
Phosphofructokinase
Escherichia coli

α + β

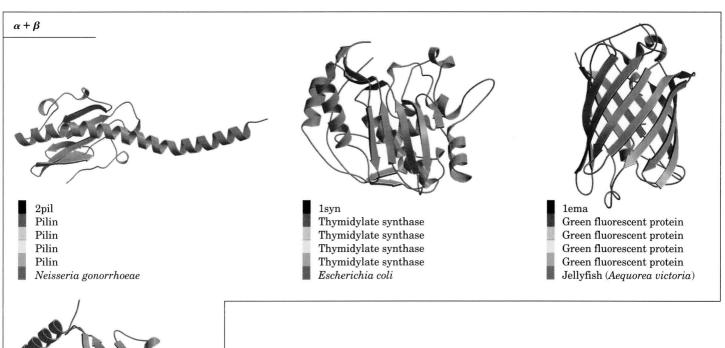

2pil
Pilin
Pilin
Pilin
Pilin
Neisseria gonorrhoeae

1syn
Thymidylate synthase
Thymidylate synthase
Thymidylate synthase
Thymidylate synthase
Escherichia coli

1ema
Green fluorescent protein
Green fluorescent protein
Green fluorescent protein
Green fluorescent protein
Jellyfish (*Aequorea victoria*)

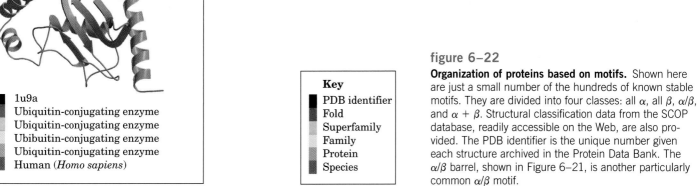

1u9a
Ubiquitin-conjugating enzyme
Ubiquitin-conjugating enzyme
Ubibuitin-conjugating enzyme
Ubiquitin-conjugating enzyme
Human (*Homo sapiens*)

Key	
■	PDB identifier
■	Fold
■	Superfamily
■	Family
■	Protein
■	Species

figure 6–22

Organization of proteins based on motifs. Shown here are just a small number of the hundreds of known stable motifs. They are divided into four classes: all α, all β, α/β, and α + β. Structural classification data from the SCOP database, readily accessible on the Web, are also provided. The PDB identifier is the unique number given each structure archived in the Protein Data Bank. The α/β barrel, shown in Figure 6–21, is another particularly common α/β motif.

Within each class are tens to hundreds of different folding arrangements, built up from increasingly identifiable substructures. Some of the substructure arrangements are very common, others have been found in just one protein. Figure 6–22 displays a variety of motifs arrayed among the four classes of protein structure. Those illustrated are just a minute sample of the hundreds of known motifs. The number of folding patterns is not infinite, however. As the rate at which new protein structures are elucidated has increased, the fraction of those structures containing a new motif has steadily declined. Fewer than 1,000 different folds or motifs may exist in all proteins. Figure 6–22 also shows how real proteins can be organized based on the presence of the motifs just discussed. The top two levels, **class** and **fold,** are purely structural. Below that level, categorization is based on evolutionary relationships.

Proteins with significant primary sequence similarity, and/or with demonstrably similar structure and function, are said to be in the same protein **family.** A strong evolutionary relationship is usually evident within a protein family. For example, the globin family has many different proteins with both structural and sequence similarity to myoglobin (as seen in the proteins used as examples in Box 6–3 and again in the next chapter).

Two or more families with little primary sequence similarity sometimes make use of the same major structural motif and have functional similarities; these families are grouped as **superfamilies.** An evolutionary relationship between the families in a superfamily is considered probable, even though time and functional distinctions, hence different adaptive pressures, may have erased many of the telltale sequence relationships.

Structural motifs become especially important in defining protein families and superfamilies. Improved classification and comparison systems for proteins lead inevitably to the elucidation of new functional relationships. Given the central role of proteins in living systems, these structural comparisons can help illuminate every aspect of biochemistry, from the evolution of individual proteins to the evolutionary history of complete metabolic pathways.

Protein Quaternary Structures Range from Simple Dimers to Large Complexes

Many proteins have multiple polypeptide subunits. The association of polypeptide chains can serve a variety of functions. Many multisubunit proteins have regulatory roles; the binding of small molecules may affect the interaction between subunits, causing large changes in the protein's activity in response to small changes in the concentration of substrate or regulatory molecules (Chapter 8). In other cases, separate subunits can take on separate but related functions, such as catalysis and regulation. Some associations, such as the fibrous proteins considered earlier in this chapter and the coat proteins of viruses, serve primarily structural roles. Some very large protein assemblies are the site of complex, multistep reactions. One example is the ribosome, site of protein synthesis, which incorporates dozens of protein subunits along with a number of structural RNA molecules.

A multisubunit protein is also referred to as a **multimer.** Multimeric proteins can have from two to hundreds of subunits. A multimer with just a few subunits is often called an **oligomer.** If a multimer is composed of a number of nonidentical subunits, the overall structure of the protein can be asymmetric and quite complicated. However, most multimers have identical subunits or repeating groups of nonidentical subunits, usually in symmetric arrangements. The repeating structural unit in such a multimeric protein, whether it is a single subunit or a group of subunits, is called a **protomer.**

The first oligomeric protein for which the three-dimensional structure was determined was hemoglobin (M_r 64,500), which contains four polypeptide chains and four heme prosthetic groups, in which the iron atoms are in the ferrous (Fe^{2+}) state (Fig. 6–17). The protein portion, called globin, consists of two α chains (141 residues each) and two β chains (146 residues each). Note that in this case α and β do not refer to secondary structures. Because hemoglobin is four times as large as myoglobin, much more time and effort were required to solve its three-dimensional structure by x-ray analysis, finally achieved by Max Perutz, John Kendrew, and their colleagues in 1959. The subunits of hemoglobin are arranged in symmetric pairs (Fig. 6–23), each pair having one α and one β subunit. Hemoglobin can therefore be described either as a tetramer or as a dimer of $\alpha\beta$ protomers.

Identical subunits of multimeric proteins are generally arranged in one or a limited set of symmetric patterns. A description of the structure of these proteins requires an understanding of conventions used to define symmetries. Oligomers can have either **rotational symmetry** or **helical symmetry;** that is, individual subunits can be superimposed on others (brought to coincidence) by rotation about one or more rotational axes, or by a helical rotation. In proteins with rotational symmetry, the subunits pack about the rotational axes to form closed structures. Proteins with helical symmetry tend to form structures that are more open-ended, with subunits added in a spiraling array.

Max Perutz (left)
John Kendrew, 1917–1997

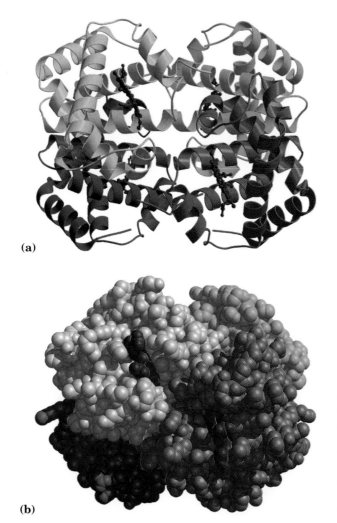

(a)

(b)

figure 6–23
The quaternary structure of deoxyhemoglobin. X-ray diffraction analysis of deoxyhemoglobin (hemoglobin without oxygen molecules bound to the heme groups) shows how the four polypeptide subunits are packed together. **(a)** A ribbon representation. **(b)** A space-filling model. The α subunits are shown in gray and light blue; the β subunits in pink and dark blue. Note that the heme groups (red) are relatively far apart.

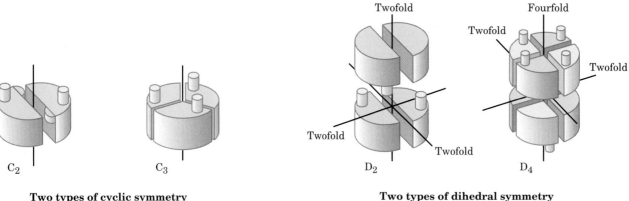

Two types of cyclic symmetry
(a)

Two types of dihedral symmetry
(b)

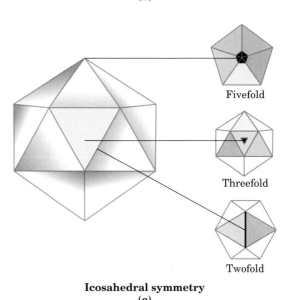

Icosahedral symmetry
(c)

figure 6–24
Rotational symmetry in proteins. (a) In cyclic symmetry, subunits are related by rotation about a single n-fold axis, where n is the number of subunits so related. The axes are shown as black lines; the numbers are values of n. Only two of many possible C_n arrangements are shown. **(b)** In dihedral symmetry, all subunits can be related by rotation about one or both of two axes, one of which is twofold. D_2 symmetry is most common. **(c)** Icosahedral symmetry. Relating all 20 triangular faces of an icosahedron requires rotation about one or more of three separate rotational axes: twofold, threefold, and fivefold. An end-on view of each of these axes is shown at the right.

There are several forms of rotational symmetry. The simplest is **cyclic symmetry,** involving rotation about a single axis (Fig. 6–24a). If subunits can be superimposed by rotation about a single axis, the protein has a symmetry defined by convention as C_n (C for cyclic, n for the number of subunits related by the axis). The axis itself is described as an n-fold rotational axis. The $\alpha\beta$ protomers of hemoglobin (Fig. 6–23) are related by C_2 symmetry. A somewhat more complicated rotational symmetry is **dihedral symmetry,** in which a twofold rotational axis intersects an n-fold axis at right angles. The symmetry is defined as D_n (Fig. 6–24b). A protein with dihedral symmetry has $2n$ protomers.

Proteins with cyclic or dihedral symmetry are particularly common. More complex rotational symmetries are possible, but only a few are regularly encountered. One example is icosahedral symmetry. An icosahedron is a regular 12-cornered polyhedron having 20 equilateral triangular faces (Fig. 6–24c). Each face can be brought to coincidence with another by rotation about one or more of three rotational axes. This is a common structure in virus coats, or capsids. The human poliovirus has an icosahedral capsid (Fig. 6–25a). Each triangular face is made up of three protomers, each protomer containing single copies of four different polypeptide chains, three of which are accessible at the outer surface. Sixty protomers form the 20 faces of the icosahedral shell enclosing the genetic material (RNA).

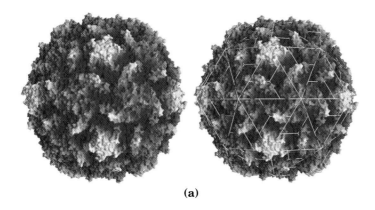

(a)

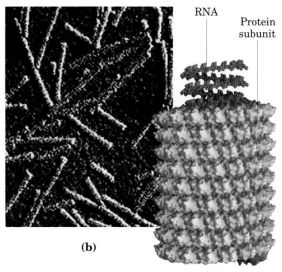

(b)

The other major type of symmetry found in oligomers, helical symmetry, also occurs in capsids. Tobacco mosaic virus is a right-handed helical filament made up of 2,130 identical subunits (Fig. 6–25b). This cylindrical structure encloses the viral RNA. Proteins with subunits arranged in helical filaments can also form long, fibrous structures such as the actin filaments of muscle (Figure 7–30).

There Are Limits to the Size of Proteins

The relatively large size of proteins reflects their functions. The function of an enzyme, for example, requires a stable structure containing a pocket large enough to bind its substrate and catalyze a reaction. Protein size has limits, however, imposed by two factors: the genetic coding capacity of nucleic acids and the accuracy of the protein biosynthetic process. The use of many copies of one or a few proteins to make a large enclosing structure (capsid) is important for viruses because this strategy conserves genetic material. Remember that there is a linear correspondence between the sequence of a gene in the nucleic acid and the amino acid sequence of the protein for which it codes. The nucleic acids of viruses are much too small to encode the information required for a protein shell made of a single polypeptide. By using many copies of much smaller polypeptides, a much shorter nucleic acid is needed for coding the capsid subunits, and this nucleic acid can be efficiently used over and over again. Cells also use large complexes of polypeptides in muscle, cilia, the cytoskeleton, and other structures. It is simply more efficient to make many copies of a small polypeptide than one copy of a very large protein. In fact, most proteins with a molecular weight greater than 100,000 have multiple subunits, identical or different. The second factor limiting the size of proteins is the error frequency during protein biosynthesis. The error frequency is low (about 1 mistake per 10,000 amino acid residues added), but even this low rate results in a high probability of a damaged protein if the protein is very large. Simply put, the potential for incorporating a "wrong" amino acid in a protein is greater for a large protein than for a small one.

Protein Denaturation and Folding

All proteins begin their existence on a ribosome as a linear sequence of amino acid residues. This polypeptide must fold during and following synthesis to take up its native conformation. We have seen that a native protein conformation is only marginally stable. Modest changes in the protein's environment can bring about structural changes that can affect function. We now explore the transition that occurs between the folded and unfolded states.

figure 6–25
Viral capsids. (a) Poliovirus. The coat proteins of poliovirus assemble into an icosahedron 300 Å in diameter. Icosahedral symmetry is a type of rotational symmetry (see Fig. 6–24c). On the left is a surface contour image of the poliovirus capsid. In the image on the right, lines have been superimposed to show the axes of symmetry. **(b)** Tobacco mosaic virus. This rod-shaped virus (as shown in the electron micrograph) is 3,000 Å long and 180 Å in diameter; it has helical symmetry.

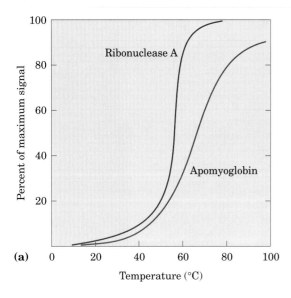

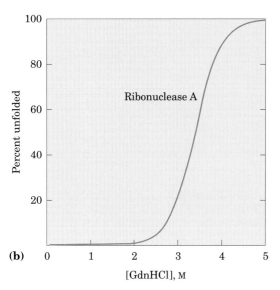

figure 6–26

Protein denaturation. Results are shown for proteins denatured by two different environmental changes. In each case, the transition from the folded to unfolded state is fairly abrupt, suggesting cooperativity in the unfolding process. **(a)** Thermal denaturation of horse apomyoglobin (myoglobin without the heme prosthetic group) and ribonuclease A (with its disulfide bonds intact; see Fig. 6–27). The midpoint of the temperature range over which denaturation occurs is called the melting temperature, or T_m. The denaturation of apomyoglobin was monitored by circular dichroism, a technique that measures the amount of helical structure in a macromolecule. Denaturation of ribonuclease A was tracked by monitoring changes in the intrinsic fluorescence of the protein, which is affected by changes in the environment of Trp residues. **(b)** Denaturation of disulfide-intact ribonuclease A by guanidine hydrochloride (GdnHCl), monitored by circular dichroism.

Loss of Protein Structure Results in Loss of Function

Protein structures have evolved to function in particular cellular environments. Conditions different from those in the cell can result in protein structural changes, large and small. A loss of three-dimensional structure sufficient to cause loss of function is called **denaturation.** The denatured state does not necessarily equate with complete unfolding of the protein and randomization of conformation. Under most conditions, denatured proteins exist in a set of partially folded states that are poorly understood.

Most proteins can be denatured by heat, which affects the weak interactions in a protein (primarily hydrogen bonds) in a complex manner. If the temperature is increased slowly, a protein's conformation generally remains intact until an abrupt loss of structure (and function) occurs over a narrow temperature range (Fig. 6–26). The abruptness of the change suggests that unfolding is a cooperative process: loss of structure in one part of the protein destabilizes other parts. The effects of heat on proteins are not yet readily predictable. The very heat-stable proteins of thermophilic bacteria have evolved to function at the temperature of hot springs (~100 °C). Yet, the structures of these proteins often differ only slightly from those of homologous proteins derived from bacteria such as *Escherichia coli.* How these small differences promote structural stability at high temperatures is not yet understood.

Proteins can be denatured not only by heat but by extremes of pH, by certain miscible organic solvents such as alcohol or acetone, by certain solutes such as urea and guanidine hydrochloride, or by detergents. Each of these denaturing agents represents a relatively mild treatment in the sense that no covalent bonds in the polypeptide chain are broken. Organic solvents, urea, and detergents act primarily by disrupting the hydrophobic interactions that make up the stable core of globular proteins; extremes of pH alter the net charge on the protein, causing electrostatic repulsion and the disruption of some hydrogen bonding. The denatured states obtained with these various treatments need not be equivalent.

Amino Acid Sequence Determines Tertiary Structure

The tertiary structure of a globular protein is determined by its amino acid sequence. The most important proof of this came from experiments showing that denaturation of some proteins is reversible. Certain globular proteins denatured by heat, extremes of pH, or denaturing reagents will regain their native structure and their biological activity if returned to conditions in which the native conformation is stable. This process is called **renaturation.**

A classic example is the denaturation and renaturation of ribonuclease. Purified ribonuclease can be completely denatured by exposure to a concentrated urea solution in the presence of a reducing agent. The reducing agent cleaves the four disulfide bonds to yield eight Cys residues, and the urea disrupts the stabilizing hydrophobic interactions, thus freeing the entire polypeptide from its folded conformation. Denaturation of ribonuclease is accompanied by a complete loss of catalytic activity. When the urea and the reducing agent are removed, the randomly coiled, denatured ribonuclease spontaneously refolds into its correct tertiary structure, with full restoration of its catalytic activity (Fig. 6–27). The refolding of ribonuclease is so accurate that the four intrachain disulfide bonds are re-formed in the same positions in the renatured molecule as in the native ribonuclease. As calculated mathematically, the eight Cys residues could recombine at random to form up to four disulfide bonds in 105 different ways. In fact, an essentially random distribution of disulfide bonds was obtained when the

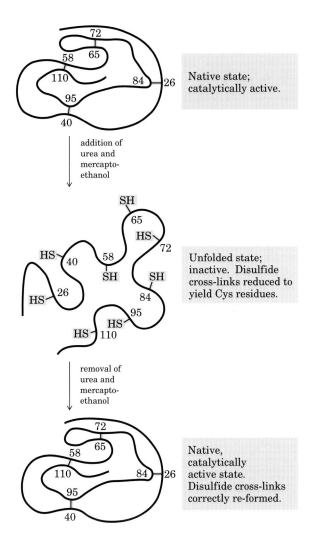

figure 6–27
Renaturation of unfolded, denatured ribonuclease. Urea is used to denature ribonuclease, and mercaptoethanol (HOCH$_2$CH$_2$SH) to reduce and thus cleave the disulfide bonds to yield eight Cys residues. Renaturation involves reestablishment of the correct disulfide cross-links.

Native state; catalytically active.

addition of urea and mercapto-ethanol

Unfolded state; inactive. Disulfide cross-links reduced to yield Cys residues.

removal of urea and mercapto-ethanol

Native, catalytically active state. Disulfide cross-links correctly re-formed.

disulfides were allowed to re-form in the presence of denaturant, indicating that weak bonding interactions are required for correct positioning of disulfide bonds and assumption of the native conformation.

This classic experiment, carried out by Christian Anfinsen in the 1950s, provided the first evidence that the amino acid sequence of a polypeptide chain contains all the information required to fold the chain into its native, three-dimensional structure. Later, similar results were obtained using chemically synthesized, catalytically active ribonuclease. This eliminated the possibility that some minor contaminant in Anfinsen's purified ribonuclease preparation might have contributed to the renaturation of the enzyme, thus dispelling any remaining doubt that this enzyme folds spontaneously.

Polypeptides Fold Rapidly by a Stepwise Process

In living cells, proteins are assembled from amino acids at a very high rate. For example, *E. coli* cells can make a complete, biologically active protein molecule containing 100 amino acid residues in about 5 s at 37 °C. How does such a polypeptide chain arrive at its native conformation? Let's assume conservatively that each of the amino acid residues could take up 10 different conformations on average, giving 10^{100} different conformations for the polypeptide. Let's also assume that the protein folds itself spontaneously by a random process in which it tries out all possible conformations around every single bond in its backbone until it finds its native, biologically active form. If each conformation were sampled in the shortest possible time ($\sim 10^{-13}$ s, or the time required for a single molecular vibration), it would take about 10^{77} yr to sample all possible conformations. Thus protein folding cannot be a completely random, trial-and-error process. There must be shortcuts. This problem was first pointed out by Cyrus Levinthal in 1968, and is sometimes called Levinthal's paradox.

The folding pathway of a large polypeptide chain is unquestionably complicated, and not all the principles that guide the process have been worked out. However, extensive study has led to the development of several plausible models. In one, the folding process is envisioned as hierarchical. Local secondary structures form first. Certain amino acid sequences fold readily into α helices or β sheets, guided by constraints we have reviewed in our discussion of secondary structure. This is followed by longer-range interactions between, say, two α helices that come together to form stable supersecondary structures. The process continues until complete domains form and the entire polypeptide is folded (Fig. 6–28). In an alternative model, folding is initiated by a spontaneous collapse of the polypeptide into a compact state, mediated by hydrophobic interactions among nonpolar residues. The state resulting from this "hydrophobic collapse" may have a high content of secondary structure, but many amino acid side chains are not entirely fixed. The collapsed state is often referred to as a **molten globule.**

Most proteins probably fold by a process that incorporates features of both models. Instead of following a single pathway, a population of peptide molecules may take a variety of routes to the same end point, with the number of different partly folded conformational species decreasing as folding nears completion.

figure 6–28

A simulated folding pathway. The folding pathway of a 36-residue subdomain of the protein villin was simulated by computer. The process started with the randomly coiled peptide and 3,000 surrounding water molecules in a virtual "water box." The molecular motions of the peptide and the effects of the water molecules were taken into account in mapping the most likely paths to the final structure among the countless alternatives. The simulated folding took place in a theoretical timespan of 1 μs; however, the calculation required half a billion integration steps on two Cray supercomputers, each running for two months. (Coordinates courtesy of Yong Duan and Peter A. Kollman, University of California at San Francisco.)

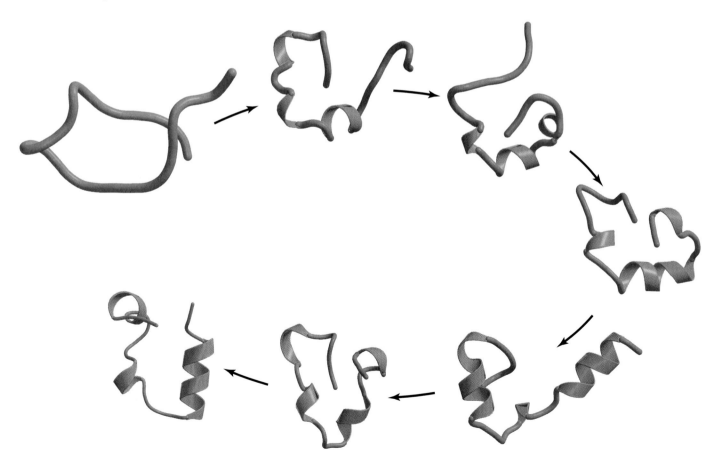

Beginning of helix formation and collapse

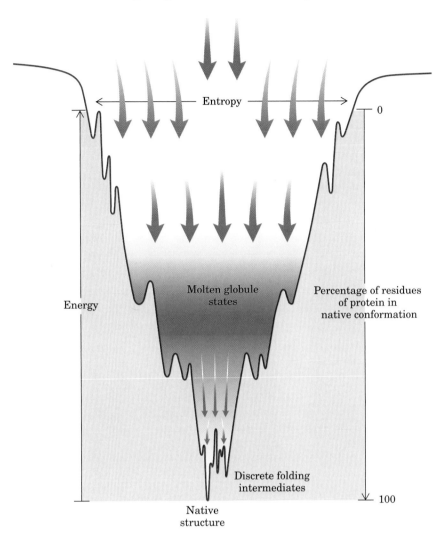

figure 6–29
The thermodynamics of protein folding depicted as a free-energy funnel. At the top, the number of conformations, and hence the conformational entropy, is large. Only a small fraction of the intramolecular interactions that will exist in the native conformation are present. As folding progresses, the thermodynamic path down the funnel reduces the number of states present (decreases entropy), increases the amount of protein in the native conformation, and decreases the free energy. Depressions on the sides of the funnel represent semistable folding intermediates, which may, in some cases, slow the folding process.

Thermodynamically, the folding process can be viewed as a kind of free-energy funnel (Fig. 6–29). The unfolded states are characterized by a high degree of conformational entropy and relatively high free energy. As folding proceeds, the narrowing of the funnel represents a decrease in the number of conformational species present. Small depressions along the sides of the free-energy funnel represent semistable intermediates that can briefly slow the folding process. At the bottom of the funnel, an ensemble of folding intermediates has been reduced to a single native conformation (or one of a small set of native conformations).

Defects in protein folding may be the molecular basis for a wide range of human genetic disorders. For example, cystic fibrosis is caused by defects in a membrane-bound protein called cystic fibrosis transmembrane conductance regulator (CFTR), which acts as a channel for chloride ions. The most common cystic fibrosis–causing mutation is the deletion of a Phe residue at position 508 in CFTR, which causes improper protein folding. Many of the disease-related mutations in collagen (p. 6-16) also cause defective folding. Improved understanding of protein folding may lead to new therapies for these and many other diseases (Box 6–4).

box 6–4   Death by Misfolding: The Prion Diseases

A misfolded protein appears to be the causative agent of a number of rare degenerative brain diseases in mammals. Perhaps the best known of these is mad cow disease, an outbreak of which made international headlines in the spring of 1996. Related diseases include kuru and Creutzfeldt-Jakob disease in humans and scrapie in sheep. The diseases are sometimes referred to as spongiform encephalopathies, so named because the diseased brain frequently becomes riddled with holes (Fig. 1). Typical symptoms include dementia and loss of coordination. These diseases are fatal.

In the 1960s, investigators found that preparations of the disease-causing agents appeared to lack nucleic acids. At this time, Tikvah Alper suggested that the agent was a protein. Initially, the idea seemed heretical. All disease-causing agents known up to that time—viruses, bacteria, fungi, and so on—contained nucleic acids, and their virulence was related to genetic reproduction and propagation. However, three decades of investigations, pursued most notably by Stanley Prusiner, have provided evidence that spongiform encephalopathies are different.

The infectious agent has been traced to a single protein (M_r 28,000), which Prusiner dubbed prion protein (PrP). Prion protein is a normal constituent of brain tissue in all mammals. Its function is not known. Strains of mice lacking the gene for PrP (and thus the protein itself) appear to suffer no ill effects. Illness occurs only when the normal cellular PrP, or PrP^C, occurs in an altered conformation called PrP^{Sc} (Sc denotes scrapie). The interaction of PrP^{Sc} with PrP^C converts the latter to PrP^{Sc}, initiating a domino effect in which more and more of the cellular protein converts to the disease-causing form. The mechanism by which the presence of PrP^{Sc} leads to spongiform encephalopathy is not understood.

In inherited forms of prion diseases, a mutation in the gene encoding PrP produces a change

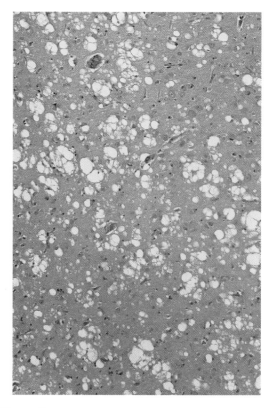

figure 1

A stained section of the cerebral cortex from a patient with Creutzfeldt-Jakob disease shows spongiform (vacuolar) degeneration, the most characteristic neurohistological feature. The vacuoles (white spots) are intracellular and occur mostly in pre- and postsynaptic processes of neurons. The vacuoles in this section vary in diameter from 20 to 100 μm.

in one amino acid residue that is believed to make the conversion of PrP^C to PrP^{Sc} more likely. A complete understanding of prion diseases awaits new information about how prion protein affects brain function, as well as more detailed structural information about both forms of PrP.

Some Proteins Undergo Assisted Folding

Not all proteins fold spontaneously as they are synthesized in the cell. Folding for many proteins is facilitated by the action of specialized proteins. **Molecular chaperones** are proteins that interact with partially folded or improperly folded polypeptides, facilitating correct folding pathways or providing microenvironments in which folding can occur. Two classes of molecular chaperones have been well-studied. Both are found in organisms ranging

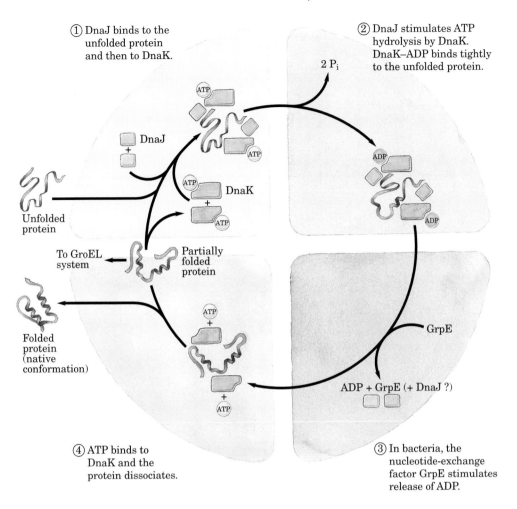

① DnaJ binds to the
unfolded protein
and then to DnaK.

② DnaJ stimulates ATP
hydrolysis by DnaK.
DnaK–ADP binds tightly
to the unfolded protein.

2 P$_i$

DnaJ

DnaK

Unfolded
protein

To GroEL
system

Partially
folded
protein

Folded
protein
(native
conformation)

GrpE

ADP + GrpE (+ DnaJ ?)

④ ATP binds to
DnaK and the
protein dissociates.

③ In bacteria, the
nucleotide-exchange
factor GrpE stimulates
release of ADP.

figure 6–30

Chaperones in protein folding. The cyclic pathway by
which chaperones bind and release polypeptides is illustrated for the *E. coli* chaperone proteins DnaK and DnaJ,
homologs of the eukaryotic chaperones Hsp70 and
Hsp40. The chaperones do not actively promote the
folding of the substrate protein, but instead prevent
aggregation of unfolded peptides. For a population of
polypeptides, some fraction of the polypeptides released
at the end of the cycle are in the native conformation.
The remainder are rebound by DnaK or are diverted to
the chaperonin system (GroEL; see Fig. 6–31). In bacteria, a protein called GrpE interacts transiently with DnaK
late in the cycle, promoting dissociation of ADP and pos-
sibly DnaJ. No eukaryotic analog of GrpE is known.

from bacteria to humans. The first class, a family of proteins called **Hsp70,**
generally have a molecular weight near 70,000 and are more abundant in
cells stressed by elevated temperatures (hence, *heat shock proteins* of M_r
70,000, or Hsp70). Hsp70 binds to regions of unfolded polypeptides that are
rich in hydrophobic residues, preventing inappropriate aggregation. These
chaperones thus "protect" proteins that have been denatured by heat and
peptides that are being synthesized (and are still unfolded). Hsp70 proteins
also block the folding of certain proteins that must remain unfolded until
they have been translocated across membranes. Some chaperones also facilitate the quaternary assembly of oligomeric proteins. The Hsp70 proteins
bind to and release polypeptides in a cycle that also involves several other
proteins (including a class called Hsp40) and ATP hydrolysis. Figure 6–30
illustrates chaperone-assisted folding as elucidated for the chaperones
DnaK and DnaJ in *E. coli,* homologs of the eukaryotic Hsp70 and Hsp40.
The DnaK and DnaJ proteins were first identified as proteins required for
in vitro replication of certain viral DNA molecules (hence the "Dna" designation).

The second class of chaperones are called **chaperonins.** These are
elaborate protein complexes required for the folding of a number of cellular proteins that do not fold spontaneously. In *E. coli* an estimated 10% to
15% of cellular proteins require the resident chaperonin system, called
GroEL/GroES, for folding under normal conditions (up to 30% require this
assistance when the cells are heat stressed). These proteins first became
known when they were found to be necessary for the growth of certain bacterial viruses (hence the designation "Gro"). Unfolded proteins are bound

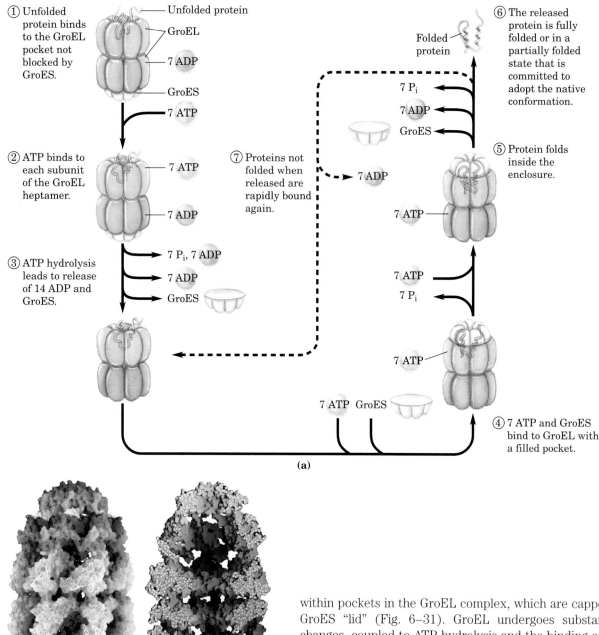

① Unfolded protein binds to the GroEL pocket not blocked by GroES.

Unfolded protein
GroEL
7 ADP
GroES
7 ATP

② ATP binds to each subunit of the GroEL heptamer.

7 ATP
7 ADP

③ ATP hydrolysis leads to release of 14 ADP and GroES.

7 P$_i$, 7 ADP
7 ADP
GroES

⑦ Proteins not folded when released are rapidly bound again.

7 ADP

⑥ The released protein is fully folded or in a partially folded state that is committed to adopt the native conformation.

Folded protein

7 P$_i$
7 ADP
GroES

⑤ Protein folds inside the enclosure.

7 ATP

7 ATP
7 P$_i$

7 ATP

7 ATP GroES

④ 7 ATP and GroES bind to GroEL with a filled pocket.

(a)

(b)

figure 6–31
Chaperonins in protein folding. (a) A proposed pathway for the action of the *E. coli* chaperonins GroEL (a member of the Hsp60 protein family) and GroES. Each GroEL complex consists of two large pockets formed by two heptameric rings (each subunit M_r 57,000). GroES, also a heptamer (subunits M_r 10,000), blocks one of the GroEL pockets. **(b)** Surface and cut-away images of the GroEL/GroES complex. The cut-away illustrates the large interior space within which other proteins are bound.

within pockets in the GroEL complex, which are capped transiently by the GroES "lid" (Fig. 6–31). GroEL undergoes substantial conformational changes, coupled to ATP hydrolysis and the binding and release of GroES, which promote folding of the bound polypeptide. Although the structure of the GroEL/GroES chaperonin is known, many details of its mechanism of action remain unresolved.

Finally, the folding pathways of a number of proteins require two enzymes that catalyze isomerization reactions. **Protein disulfide isomerase (PDI)** is a widely distributed enzyme that catalyzes the interchange or shuffling of disulfide bonds until the bonds of the native conformation are formed. Among its functions, PDI catalyzes the elimination of folding intermediates with inappropriate disulfide cross-links. **Peptide prolyl cis-trans isomerase (PPI)** catalyzes the interconversion of the cis and trans isomers of proline peptide bonds (Fig. 6–8b), which can be a slow step in the folding of proteins that contain some bonds in the cis conformation.

Protein folding is likely to be a more complex process in the densely packed cellular environment than in the test tube. More classes of proteins that facilitate protein folding may be discovered as the biochemical dissection of the folding process continues.

summary

Every protein has a unique three-dimensional structure that reflects its function. Protein structure is stabilized by multiple weak interactions. Hydrophobic interactions provide the major contribution to stabilizing the globular form of most soluble proteins; hydrogen bonds and ionic interactions are optimized in the specific structure that is thermodynamically most stable.

The nature of the covalent bonds in the polypeptide chain places constraints on structure. The peptide bond exhibits partial double-bond character that keeps the entire peptide group in a rigid planar configuration. The N—C_α and C_α—C bonds can rotate with bond angles ϕ and ψ, respectively. Secondary structure can be defined completely if the ϕ and ψ angles are known for all amino acid residues in that polypeptide segment.

Tertiary structure, the complete three-dimensional structure of a polypeptide chain, can be understood by examining common, stable substructures variably called supersecondary structures, motifs, or folds. Motifs range from simple to very complex. The thousands of known protein structures are generally assembled from a repertoire of only a few hundred motifs, some of which are very common. Regions of a polypeptide chain that can fold stably and independently are called domains. Small proteins generally have only a single domain, whereas large proteins may have several.

There are two general classes of proteins: fibrous and globular. Fibrous proteins, which serve mainly structural roles, have simple repeating elements of secondary structure and were models for early studies of protein structure. Two major types of secondary structure were predicted by model building based on information obtained from fibrous proteins: the α helix and the β conformation. Both are characterized by optimal hydrogen bonding between peptide bonds in the polypeptide backbone. The stability of these structures within a protein is influenced by their amino acid content and by the relative placement of amino acid residues in the sequence. Another type of secondary structure common in proteins is the β turn.

In fibrous proteins such as keratins and collagen, a single type of secondary structure predominates. The polypeptide chains are supercoiled into ropes and then combined in larger bundles to provide strength. The β sheets of silk fibroin are stacked to build a strong but flexible structure.

Globular proteins have more complicated tertiary structures, often containing several types of secondary structure in the same polypeptide chain. The first globular protein structure to be determined, using x-ray diffraction methods, was that of myoglobin. This structure confirmed that a predicted secondary structure (α helix) occurs in proteins; that hydrophobic amino acid residues are located in the protein interior; and that globular proteins are compact. Subsequent research on the structure of many globular proteins has reinforced these conclusions while demonstrating that great variety can be found in tertiary structure.

The complex structures of globular proteins can be analyzed by examining substructures, including motifs and domains. In protein structural databases, structures are commonly organized into four major classes: all α, all β, α/β, and $\alpha + \beta$. Specific proteins in each class are grouped into families and superfamilies based on correlations in sequence, structure, and function.

Quaternary structure refers to the interaction between the subunits of multisubunit (multimeric) proteins or large protein assemblies. Some multimeric proteins have a repeated unit consisting of a single subunit or a group of subunits referred to as a protomer. The protomers are usually related by rotational or helical symmetry. The best-studied multimeric protein is hemoglobin.

The three-dimensional structure of proteins can be destroyed by treatments that disrupt weak interactions, a process called denaturation. Denaturation destroys protein function, demonstrating a relationship between structure and function. Some denatured proteins (e.g., ribonuclease) can renature spontaneously to form biologically active protein, showing that the tertiary structure of a protein is determined by its amino acid sequence.

Protein folding in cells probably involves multiple pathways. Initially, regions of secondary structure may form, followed by folding into supersecondary structures. Large ensembles of folding intermediates are rapidly brought to a single native conformation. For many proteins, folding is facilitated by Hsp70 chaperones and by chaperonins. Disulfide bond formation and the cis-trans isomerization of proline peptide bonds are catalyzed by specific enzymes.

further reading

General

Anfinsen, C.B. (1973) Principles that govern the folding of protein chains. *Science* **181,** 223–230.

The author reviews his classic work on ribonuclease.

Branden, C. & Tooze, J. (1991) *Introduction to Protein Structure,* Garland Publishing, Inc., New York.

Creighton, T.E. (1993) *Proteins: Structures and Molecular Properties,* 2nd edn, W.H. Freeman and Company, New York.

A comprehensive and authoritative source.

Evolution of Catalytic Function. (1987) *Cold Spring Harb. Symp. Quant. Biol.* **52.**

A source of excellent articles on many topics, including protein structure, folding, and function.

Kendrew, J.C. (1961) The three-dimensional structure of a protein molecule. *Sci. Am.* **205** (December), 96–111.

Describes how the structure of myoglobin was determined and what was learned from it.

Richardson, J.S. (1981) The anatomy and taxonomy of protein structure. *Adv. Prot. Chem.* **34,** 167–339.

An outstanding summary of protein structural patterns and principles; the author originated the very useful "ribbon" representations of protein structure.

Secondary, Tertiary, and Quaternary Structure

Brenner, S.E., Chothia, C., & Hubbard, T.J.P. (1997) Population statistics of protein structures: lessons from structural classifications. *Curr. Opin. Struct. Biol.* **7,** 369–376.

Chothia, C., Hubbard, T., Brenner, S., Barns, H., & Murzin, A. (1997) Protein folds in the all-β and all-α classes. *Annu. Rev. Physiol. Biomol. Struct.* **26,** 597–627.

Fuchs, E. & Cleveland, D.W. (1998) A structural scaffolding of intermediate filaments in health and disease. *Science* **279,** 514–519.

McPherson, A. (1989) Macromolecular crystals. *Sci. Am.* **260** (March), 62–69.

Describes how macromolecules such as proteins are crystallized.

Prockop, D.J. & Kivirikko, K.I. (1995) Collagens, molecular biology, diseases, and potentials for therapy. *Annu. Rev. Biochem.* **64,** 403–434.

Shoeman, R.L. & Traub, P. (1993) Assembly of intermediate filaments. *Bioessays* **15,** 605–611.

Protein Denaturation and Folding

Aurora, R., Creamer, T.P., Srinivasan, R., & Rose, G.D. (1997) Local interactions in protein folding: lessons from the α-helix. *J. Biol. Chem.* **272,** 1413–1416.

Baldwin, R.L. (1994) Matching speed and stability. *Nature* **369,** 183–184.

Creighton, T.E., Darby, N.J., & Kemmink, J. (1996) The roles of partly folded intermediates in protein folding. *FASEB J.* **10,** 110–118.

Dill, K.A. & Chan, H.S. (1997) From Levinthal to pathways to funnels. *Nat. Struct. Biol.* **4,** 10–19.

Johnson, J.L. & Craig, E.A. (1997) Protein folding *in vivo*: unraveling complex pathways. *Cell* **90,** 201–204.

Netzer, W.J. & Hartl, F.U. (1998) Protein folding in the cytosol: chaperonin-dependent and independent mechanisms. *Trends Biochem. Sci.* **23,** 68–73.

Prusiner, S.B. (1995) The prion diseases. *Sci. Am.* **272** (January), 48–57.

Prusiner, S.B., Scott, M.R., DeArmond, S.J., & Cohen, F.E. (1998) Prion protein biology. *Cell* **93,** 337–348.

Richardson, A., Landry, S.J., & Georgopolous, C. (1998) The ins and outs of a molecular chaperone machine. *Trends Biochem. Sci.* **23,** 138–143.

Ruddon, R.R. & Bedows, E. (1997) Assisted protein folding. *J. Biol. Chem.* **272,** 3125–3128.

Thomas, P.J., Qu, B-H., & Pederson, P.L. (1995) Defective protein folding as a basis of human disease. *Trends Biochem. Sci.* **20,** 456–459.

problems

1. Properties of the Peptide Bond In x-ray studies of crystalline peptides, Linus Pauling and Robert Corey found that the C—N bond in the peptide link is intermediate in length (1.32 Å) between a typical C—N single bond (1.49 Å) and a C=N double bond (1.27 Å). They also found that the peptide bond is planar (all four atoms attached to the C—N group are located in the same plane) and that the two α-carbon atoms attached to the C—N are always trans to each other (on opposite sides of the peptide bond):

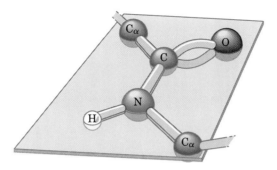

(a) What does the length of the C—N bond in the peptide linkage indicate about its strength and its bond order (i.e., whether it is single, double, or triple)?

(b) What do the observations of Pauling and Corey tell us about the ease of rotation about the C—N peptide bond?

2. Structural and Functional Relationships in Fibrous Proteins William Astbury discovered that the x-ray pattern of wool shows a repeating structural unit spaced about 5.2 Å along the direction of the wool fiber. When he steamed and stretched the wool, the x-ray pattern showed a new repeating structural unit at a spacing of 7.0 Å. Steaming and stretching the wool and then letting it shrink gave an x-ray pattern consistent with the original spacing of about 5.2 Å. Although these observations provided important clues to the molecular structure of wool, Astbury was unable to interpret them at the time.

(a) Given our current understanding of the structure of wool, interpret Astbury's observations.

(b) When wool sweaters or socks are washed in hot water or heated in a dryer, they shrink. Silk, on the other hand, does not shrink under the same conditions. Explain.

3. Rate of Synthesis of Hair α-Keratin Hair grows at a rate of 15 to 20 cm/yr. All this growth is concentrated at the base of the hair fiber, where α-keratin filaments are synthesized inside living epidermal cells and assembled into ropelike structures (see Fig. 6–11). The fundamental structural element of α-keratin is the α helix, which has 3.6 amino acid residues per turn and a rise of 5.4 Å per turn (see Fig. 6–4b). Assuming that the biosynthesis of α-helical keratin chains is the rate-limiting factor in the growth of hair, calculate the rate at which peptide bonds of α-keratin chains must be synthesized (peptide bonds per second) to account for the observed yearly growth of hair.

4. The Effect of pH on the Conformation of α-Helical Secondary Structures The unfolding of the α helix of a polypeptide to a randomly coiled conformation is accompanied by a large decrease in a property called its specific rotation, a measure of a solution's capacity to rotate plane-polarized light. Polyglutamate, a polypeptide made up of only L-Glu residues, has the α-helical conformation at pH 3. However, when the pH is raised to 7, there is a large decrease in the specific rotation of the solution. Similarly, polylysine (L-Lys residues) is an α helix at pH 10, but

when the pH is lowered to 7 the specific rotation also decreases, as shown by the following graph.

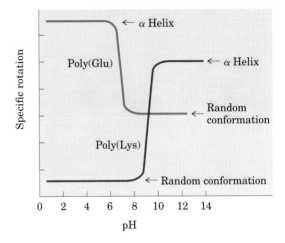

What is the explanation for the effect of the pH changes on the conformations of poly(Glu) and poly(Lys)? Why does the transition occur over such a narrow range of pH?

5. Disulfide Bonds Determine the Properties of Many Proteins A number of natural proteins are very rich in disulfide bonds, and their mechanical properties (tensile strength, viscosity, hardness, etc.) are correlated with the degree of disulfide bonding. For example, glutenin, a wheat protein rich in disulfide bonds, is responsible for the cohesive and elastic character of dough made from wheat flour. Similarly, the hard, tough nature of tortoise shell is due to the extensive disulfide bonding in its α-keratin.

(a) What is the molecular basis for the correlation between disulfide-bond content and mechanical properties of the protein?

(b) Most globular proteins are denatured and lose their activity when briefly heated to 65 °C. However, globular proteins that contain multiple disulfide bonds often must be heated longer at higher temperatures to denature them. One such protein is bovine pancreatic trypsin inhibitor (BPTI), which has 58 amino acid residues in a single chain and contains three disulfide bonds. On cooling a solution of denatured BPTI, the activity of the protein is restored. What is the molecular basis for this property?

6. Amino Acid Sequence and Protein Structure Our growing understanding of how proteins fold allows researchers to make predictions about protein structure based on primary amino acid sequence data.

1	2	3	4	5	6	7	8	9	10
Ile –	Ala –	His –	Thr –	Tyr –	Gly –	Pro –	Phe –	Glu –	Ala –

11	12	13	14	15	16	17	18	19	20
Ala –	Met –	Cys –	Lys –	Trp –	Glu –	Ala –	Gln –	Pro –	Asp –

21	22	23	24	25	26	27	28
Gly –	Met –	Glu –	Cys –	Ala –	Phe –	His –	Arg

(a) Based on the amino acid sequence above, where would you predict that bends or β turns would occur?

(b) Where might intrachain disulfide cross-linkages be formed?

(c) Assuming that this sequence is part of a larger globular protein, indicate the probable location (the external surface or interior of the protein) of the following amino acid residues: Asp, Ile, Thr, Ala, Gln, Lys. Explain your reasoning. (Hint: See the hydropathy index in Table 5–1).

7. Bacteriorhodopsin in Purple Membrane Proteins Under the proper environmental conditions, the salt-loving bacterium *Halobacterium halobium* synthesizes a membrane protein (M_r 26,000) known as bacteriorhodopsin, which is purple because it contains retinal. Molecules of this protein aggregate into "purple patches" in the cell membrane. Bacteriorhodopsin acts as a light-activated proton pump that provides energy for cell functions. X-ray analysis of this protein reveals that it consists of seven parallel α-helical segments, each of which traverses the bacterial cell membrane (thickness 45 Å). Calculate the minimum number of amino acid residues necessary for one segment of α helix to traverse the membrane completely. Estimate the fraction of the bacteriorhodopsin protein that is involved in membrane-spanning helices. (Use an average amino acid residue weight of 110.)

8. Pathogenic Action of Bacteria That Cause Gas Gangrene The highly pathogenic anaerobic bacterium *Clostridium perfringens* is responsible for gas gangrene, a condition in which animal tissue structure is destroyed. This bacterium secretes an enzyme that efficiently catalyzes the hydrolysis of the peptide bond indicated in red in the sequence:

$$-\text{X}-\text{Gly}-\text{Pro}-\text{Y}- \xrightarrow{\text{H}_2\text{O}}$$
$$-\text{X}-\text{COO}^- + \text{H}_3\overset{+}{\text{N}}-\text{Gly}-\text{Pro}-\text{Y}-$$

where X and Y are any of the 20 standard amino acids. How does the secretion of this enzyme contribute to the invasiveness of this bacterium in human tissues? Why does this enzyme not affect the bacterium itself?

9. Number of Polypeptide Chains in a Multisubunit Protein A sample (660 mg) of an oligomeric protein of M_r 132,000 was treated with an excess of 1-fluoro-2,4-dinitrobenzene (Sanger's reagent) under slightly alkaline conditions until the chemical reaction was complete. The peptide bonds of the protein were then completely hydrolyzed by heating it with concentrated HCl. The hydrolysate was found to contain 5.5 mg of the following compound:

However, 2,4-dinitrophenyl derivatives of the α-amino groups of other amino acids could not be found.

(a) Explain how this information can be used to determine the number of polypeptide chains in an oligomeric protein.

(b) Calculate the number of polypeptide chains in this protein.

(c) What other protein analysis technique could you employ to determine whether the polypeptide chains in this protein are similar or different?

Biochemistry on the Internet

10. Protein Modeling on the Internet A group of patients suffering from Crohn's disease (an inflammatory bowel disease) underwent biopsies of their intestinal mucosa in an attempt to identify the causative agent. A protein was identified that was expressed at higher levels in patients with Crohn's disease than in patients with an unrelated inflammatory bowel disease or in unaffected controls. The protein was isolated and the following *partial* amino acid sequence was obtained:

EAELCPDRCI	HSFQNLGIQC	VKKRDLEQAI
SQRIQTNNNP	FQVPIEEQRG	DYDLNAVRLC
FQVTVRDPSG	RPLRLPPVLP	HPIFDNRAPN
TAELKICRVN	RNSGSCLGGD	EIFLLCDKVQ
KEDIEVYFTG	PGWEARGSFS	QADVHRQVAI
VFRTPPYADP	SLQAPVRVSM	QLRRPSDREL
SEPMEFQYLP	DTDDRHRIEE	KRKRTYETFK
SIMKKSPFSG	PTDPRPPPRR	IAVPSRSSAS
VPKPAPQPYP		

(a) You can identify this protein using a protein database on the Internet. Some good places to start include PIR-International Protein Sequence Database, Structural Classification of Proteins (SCOP), and Prosite. For the current URLs of these and other protein database sites, use an Internet search engine or go to the *Principles of Biochemistry*, 3/e site at http://www.worthpublishers.com.

At these sites, follow links to locate the sequence comparison "engine." Enter about 30 residues from the sequence of the protein in the appropriate search field and submit it for analysis. What does this analysis tell you about the identity of the protein?

(b) Try using different portions of the protein amino acid sequence. Do you always get the same result?

(c) A variety of web sites provide information about the three-dimensional structure of proteins. Find information about the protein's secondary, tertiary, and quaternary structure using database sites such as the Protein Data Bank (PDB) or SCOP.

(d) In the course of your web searches try to find information about the cellular function of the protein.

Protein Function

Knowing the three-dimensional structure of a protein is an important part of understanding how the protein functions. However, the structure shown in two dimensions on a page is deceptively static. Proteins are dynamic molecules whose functions almost invariably depend on interactions with other molecules, and these interactions are affected in physiologically important ways by sometimes subtle, sometimes striking changes in protein conformation.

In this chapter, we explore how proteins interact with other molecules and how their interactions are related to dynamic protein structure. The importance of molecular interactions to a protein's function can hardly be overemphasized. In Chapter 6, we saw that the function of fibrous proteins as structural elements of cells and tissues depends on stable, long-term quaternary interactions between identical polypeptide chains. As we will see in this chapter, the functions of many other proteins involve interactions with a variety of different molecules. Most of these interactions are fleeting, though they may be the basis of complex physiological processes such as oxygen transport, immune function, and muscle contraction, the topics we examine in detail in this chapter. The proteins that carry out these processes illustrate the following key principles of protein function, some of which will be familiar from the previous chapter:

The functions of many proteins involve the reversible binding of other molecules. A molecule bound reversibly by a protein is called a **ligand.** A ligand may be any kind of molecule, including another protein. The transient nature of protein-ligand interactions is critical to life, allowing an organism to respond rapidly and reversibly to changing environmental and metabolic circumstances.

A ligand binds at a site on the protein called the **binding site,** which is complementary to the ligand in size, shape, charge, and hydrophobic or hydrophilic character. Furthermore, the interaction is specific: the protein can discriminate among the thousands of different molecules in its environment and selectively bind only one or a few. A given protein may have separate binding sites for several different ligands. These specific molecular interactions are crucial in maintaining the high degree of order in a living system. (This discussion excludes the binding of water, which may interact weakly and nonspecifically with many parts of a protein. In Chapter 8, we consider water as a specific ligand for many enzymes.)

Proteins are flexible. Changes in conformation may be subtle, reflecting molecular vibrations and small movements of amino acid residues throughout the protein. A protein flexing in this way is sometimes said to "breathe." Changes in conformation may also be quite dramatic, with major segments of the protein structure moving as much as several nanometers. Specific conformational changes are frequently essential to a protein's function.

The binding of a protein and ligand is often coupled to a conformational change in the protein that makes the binding site more complementary to the ligand, permitting tighter binding. The structural adaptation that occurs between protein and ligand is called **induced fit.**

In a multisubunit protein, a conformational change in one subunit often affects the conformation of other subunits.

Interactions between ligands and proteins may be regulated, usually through specific interactions with one or more additional ligands. These other ligands may cause conformational changes in the protein that affect the binding of the first ligand.

Enzymes represent a special case of protein function. Enzymes bind and chemically transform other molecules—they catalyze reactions. The molecules acted upon by enzymes are called reaction **substrates** rather than ligands, and the ligand-binding site is called the **catalytic site** or **active site.** In this chapter we emphasize the noncatalytic functions of proteins. In Chapter 8 we consider catalysis by enzymes, a central topic in biochemistry. You will see that the themes of this chapter—binding, specificity, and conformational change—are continued in the next chapter, with the added element of proteins acting as reactants in chemical transformations.

Reversible Binding of a Protein to a Ligand: Oxygen-Binding Proteins

Myoglobin and hemoglobin may be the most-studied and best-understood proteins. They were the first proteins for which three-dimensional structures were determined, and our current understanding of myoglobin and hemoglobin is garnered from the work of thousands of biochemists over several decades. Most important, they illustrate almost every aspect of that most central of biochemical processes: the reversible binding of a ligand to a protein. This classic model of protein function will tell us a great deal about how proteins work.

Oxygen Can Be Bound to a Heme Prosthetic Group

Oxygen is poorly soluble in aqueous solutions and cannot be carried to tissues in sufficient quantity if it is simply dissolved in blood serum. Diffusion of oxygen through tissues is also ineffective over distances greater than a few millimeters. The evolution of larger, multicellular animals depended on the evolution of proteins that could transport and store oxygen. However, none of the amino acid side chains in proteins is suited for the reversible binding of oxygen molecules. This role is filled by certain transition metals, among them iron and copper, that have a strong tendency to bind oxygen. Multicellular organisms exploit the properties of metals, most commonly iron, for oxygen transport. However, free iron promotes the formation of highly reactive oxygen species such as hydroxyl radicals that can damage DNA and other macromolecules. Iron used in cells is therefore bound in forms that sequester it and/or make it less reactive. In multicellular organisms—especially those in which iron, in its oxygen-carrying capacity, must be transported over large distances—iron is often incorporated into a protein-bound prosthetic group called **heme.** (A prosthetic group is a compound permanently associated with a protein that contributes to the protein's function.)

figure 7-1
Heme. The heme group is present in myoglobin, hemoglobin, and many other proteins, designated heme proteins. Heme consists of a complex organic ring structure, protoporphyrin IX, to which is bound an iron atom in its ferrous (Fe^{2+}) state. Porphyrins, of which protoporphyrin IX is only one example, consist of four pyrrole rings linked by methene bridges **(a)**, with substitutions at one or more of the positions denoted X. Two representations of heme are shown in **(b)** and **(c)**. The iron atom of heme has six coordination bonds: four in the plane of, and bonded to, the flat porphyrin ring system, and two perpendicular to it **(d)**.

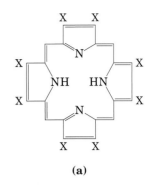

(a)

Heme (or haem) consists of a complex organic ring structure, **protoporphyrin,** to which is bound a single iron atom in its ferrous (Fe^{2+}) state (Fig. 7-1). The iron atom has six coordination bonds, four to nitrogen atoms that are part of the flat **porphyrin ring** system and two perpendicular to the porphyrin. The coordinated nitrogen atoms (which have an electron-donating character) help prevent conversion of the heme iron to the ferric (Fe^{3+}) state. Iron in the Fe^{2+} state binds oxygen reversibly; in the Fe^{3+} state it does not bind oxygen. Heme is found in a number of oxygen-transporting proteins, as well as in some proteins, such as the cytochromes, that participate in oxidation-reduction (electron transfer) reactions.

In free heme molecules, reaction of oxygen at one of the two "open" coordination bonds of iron (perpendicular to the plane of the porphyrin molecule, above and below) can result in irreversible conversion of Fe^{2+} to Fe^{3+}. In heme-containing proteins, this reaction is prevented by sequestering the heme deep within a protein structure where access to the two open coordination bonds is restricted. One of these two coordination bonds is occupied by a side-chain nitrogen of a His residue. The other is the binding site for molecular oxygen (O_2) (Fig. 7-2). When oxygen binds, the electronic properties of heme iron change; this accounts for the change in color from the dark purple of oxygen-depleted venous blood to the bright red of oxygen-rich arterial blood. Some small molecules, such as carbon monoxide (CO) and nitric oxide (NO), coordinate to heme iron with greater affinity than does O_2. When a molecule of CO is bound to heme, O_2 is excluded, which is why CO is highly toxic to aerobic organisms. By surrounding and sequestering heme, oxygen-binding proteins regulate the access of CO and other small molecules to heme iron.

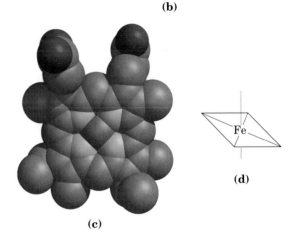

(b)

(c)

(d)

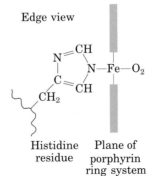

Edge view

Histidine
residue

Plane of
porphyrin
ring system

figure 7-2
The heme group viewed from the side. This view shows the two coordination bonds to Fe^{2+} perpendicular to the porphyrin ring system. One of these two bonds is occupied by a His residue, sometimes called the proximal His. The other is the binding site for oxygen. The remaining four coordination bonds are in the plane of, and bonded to, the flat porphyrin ring system.

Myoglobin Has a Single Binding Site for Oxygen

Myoglobin (M_r 16,700; abbreviated Mb) is a relatively simple oxygen-binding protein found in almost all mammals, primarily in muscle tissue. It is particularly abundant in the muscles of diving mammals such as seals and whales that must store enough oxygen for prolonged excursions undersea. Proteins very similar to myoglobin are widely distributed, occurring even in some single-celled organisms. Myoglobin stores oxygen for periods when energy demands are high and facilitates its distribution to oxygen-starved tissues.

Myoglobin is a single polypeptide of 153 amino acid residues with one molecule of heme. It is typical of the family of proteins called **globins,** which have similar primary and tertiary structures. The polypeptide is made up of eight α-helical segments connected by bends (Fig. 7–3). About 78% of the amino acid residues in the protein are found in these α helices.

Any detailed discussion of protein function inevitably involves protein structure. Our treatment of myoglobin will be facilitated by introducing some structural conventions peculiar to globins. As seen in Figure 7–3, the helical segments are labeled A through H. An individual amino acid residue may be designated either by its position in the amino acid sequence or by its location within the sequence of a particular α-helical segment. For example, the His residue coordinated to the heme in myoglobin, His[93] (the 93rd amino acid residue from the amino-terminal end of the myoglobin polypeptide sequence), is also called His F8 (the 8th residue in α helix F). The bends in the structure are labeled AB, CD, EF, and so forth, reflecting the α-helical segments they connect.

Protein-Ligand Interactions Can Be Described Quantitatively

The function of myoglobin depends on the protein's ability not only to bind oxygen, but also to release it when and where it is needed. Function in biochemistry often revolves around a reversible protein-ligand interaction of this type. A quantitative description of this interaction is therefore a central part of many biochemical investigations.

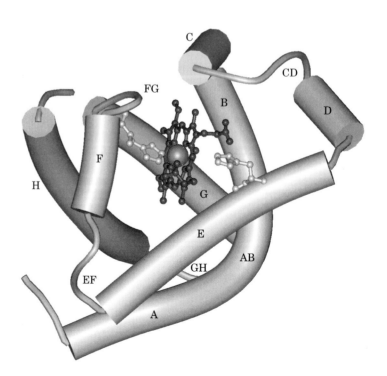

figure 7–3

The structure of myoglobin. The eight α-helical segments (shown here as cylinders) are labeled A through H. Nonhelical residues in the bends that connect them are labeled AB, CD, EF, and so forth, indicating the segments they interconnect. A few bends, including BC and DE, are abrupt and do not contain any residues; these are not normally labeled. (The short segment visible between D and E is an artifact of the computer representation.) The heme is bound in a pocket made up largely of the E and F helices, although amino acid residues from other segments of the protein also participate.

In general, the reversible binding of a protein (P) to a ligand (L) can be described by a simple **equilibrium expression:**

$$P + L \rightleftharpoons PL \qquad (7\text{–}1)$$

The reaction is characterized by an equilibrium constant, K_a, such that

$$K_a = \frac{[PL]}{[P][L]} \qquad (7\text{–}2)$$

The term $\boldsymbol{K_a}$ is an **association constant** (not to be confused with the K_a that denotes an acid dissociation constant). The association constant provides a measure of the affinity of the ligand L for the protein. K_a has units of M^{-1}; a higher value of K_a corresponds to a higher affinity of the ligand for the protein. A rearrangement of Equation 7–2 shows that the ratio of bound to free protein is directly proportional to the concentration of free ligand:

$$K_a[L] = \frac{[PL]}{[P]} \qquad (7\text{–}3)$$

When the concentration of the ligand is much greater than the concentration of ligand-binding sites, the binding of the ligand by the protein does not appreciably change the concentration of free (unbound) ligand—that is, [L] remains constant. This condition is broadly applicable to most ligands that bind to proteins in cells and simplifies our description of the binding equilibrium.

Thus we can consider the binding equilibrium from the standpoint of the fraction, θ (theta), of ligand-binding sites on the protein that are occupied by ligand:

$$\theta = \frac{\text{binding sites occupied}}{\text{total binding sites}} = \frac{[PL]}{[PL] + [P]} \qquad (7\text{–}4)$$

Substituting $K_a[L][P]$ for [PL] (see Eqn 7–3) and rearranging terms gives

$$\theta = \frac{K_a[L][P]}{K_a[L][P] + [P]} = \frac{K_a[L]}{K_a[L] + 1} = \frac{[L]}{[L] + \dfrac{1}{K_a}} \qquad (7\text{–}5)$$

The term K_a can be determined from a plot of θ versus the concentration of free ligand, [L] (Fig. 7–4a). Any equation of the form $x = y/(y + z)$ describes a hyperbola, and θ is thus found to be a hyperbolic function of [L]. The fraction of ligand-binding sites occupied approaches saturation asymptotically as [L] increases. The [L] at which half of the available ligand-binding sites are occupied (at $\theta = 0.5$) corresponds to $1/K_a$.

figure 7–4
Graphical representations of ligand binding. The fraction of ligand-binding sites occupied, θ, is plotted against the concentration of free ligand. Both curves are rectangular hyperbolas. **(a)** A hypothetical binding curve for a ligand L. The [L] at which half of the available ligand-binding sites are occupied is equivalent to $1/K_a$, or K_d. The curve has a horizontal asymptote at $\theta = 1$ and a vertical asymptote (not shown) at [L] = $-1/K_a$. **(b)** A curve describing the binding of oxygen to myoglobin. The partial pressure of O_2 in the air above the solution is expressed in terms of kilopascals (kPa). Oxygen binds tightly to myoglobin with a P_{50} of only 0.26 kPa.

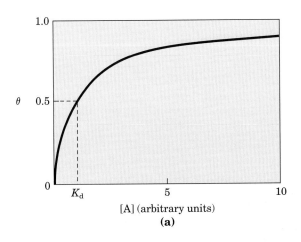

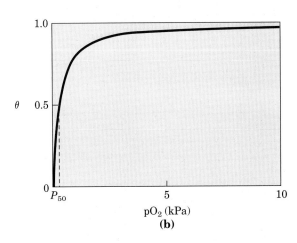

It is sometimes intuitively simpler to consider the **dissociation constant, K_d,** which is the reciprocal of K_a ($K_d = 1/K_a$) and is given in units of molar concentration (M). K_d is the equilibrium constant for the release of ligand. The relevant expressions change to

$$K_d = \frac{[P][L]}{[PL]} \tag{7-6}$$

$$[PL] = \frac{[P][L]}{K_d} \tag{7-7}$$

$$\theta = \frac{[L]}{[L] + K_d} \tag{7-8}$$

When [L] is equal to K_d, half of the ligand-binding sites are occupied. When [L] is lower than K_d, little ligand binds to the protein. In order for 90% of the available ligand-binding sites to be occupied, [L] must be nine times greater than K_d. In practice, K_d is used much more often than K_a to express the affinity of a protein for a ligand. Note that a lower value of K_d corresponds to a higher affinity of ligand for the protein. The mathematics can be reduced to simple statements: K_d is the molar concentration of ligand at which half of the available ligand-binding sites are occupied. At this point, the protein is said to have reached half saturation with respect to ligand binding. The more tightly a protein binds a ligand, the lower the concentration of ligand required for half the binding sites to be occupied, and thus the lower the value of K_d. Some representative dissociation constants are given in Table 7–1.

The binding of oxygen to myoglobin follows the patterns discussed above, but because oxygen is a gas, we must make some minor adjustments to the equations. We can simply substitute the concentration of dissolved oxygen for [L] in Equation 7–8 to give

$$\theta = \frac{[O_2]}{[O_2] + K_d} \tag{7-9}$$

As for any ligand, K_d is equal to the $[O_2]$ at which half of the available ligand-binding sites are occupied, or $[O_2]_{0.5}$. Equation 7–9 becomes

$$\theta = \frac{[O_2]}{[O_2] + [O_2]_{0.5}} \tag{7-10}$$

table 7–1

Some Protein Dissociation Constants

Protein	Ligand	K_d (M)*
Avidin (egg white)[†]	Biotin	1×10^{-15}
Insulin receptor (human)	Insulin	1×10^{-10}
Anti-HIV immunoglobulin (human)[‡]	gp41 (HIV-1 surface protein)	4×10^{-10}
Nickel-binding protein (E. coli)	Ni^{2+}	1×10^{-7}
Calmodulin (rat)[§]	Ca^{2+}	3×10^{-6}
		2×10^{-5}

*A reported dissociation constant is valid only for the particular solution conditions under which it was measured. K_d values for a protein-ligand interaction can be altered, sometimes by several orders of magnitude, by changes in solution salt concentration, pH, or other variables.

[†]Interaction of avidin with the enzymatic cofactor biotin is among the strongest noncovalent biochemical interactions known.

[‡]This immunoglobulin was isolated as part of an effort to develop a vaccine against HIV. Immunoglobulins (described later in the chapter) are highly variable, and the K_d reported here should not be considered characteristic of all immunoglobulins.

[§]Calmodulin has four binding sites for calcium. The values shown reflect the highest- and lowest-affinity binding sites observed in one set of measurements.

The concentration of a volatile substance in solution, however, is always proportional to its partial pressure in the gas phase above the solution. In experiments using oxygen as a ligand, it is the partial pressure of oxygen, pO_2, that is varied because this is easier to measure than the concentration of dissolved oxygen. If we define the partial pressure of oxygen at $[O_2]_{0.5}$ as P_{50}, substitution in Equation 7–10 gives

$$\theta = \frac{pO_2}{pO_2 + P_{50}} \qquad (7\text{–}11)$$

A binding curve for myoglobin that relates θ to pO_2 is shown in Figure 7–4b.

Protein Structure Affects How Ligands Bind

The binding of a ligand to a protein is rarely as simple as the above equations would suggest. The interaction is greatly affected by protein structure and is often accompanied by conformational changes. For example, the specificity with which heme binds its various ligands is altered when the heme is a component of myoglobin. CO binds to free heme molecules over 20,000 times better than does O_2 (the K_d or P_{50} for CO binding is more than 20,000 times lower than that for O_2) but binds only about 200 times better when the heme is bound in myoglobin. The difference is partly explained by steric hindrance. When O_2 binds to free heme, the axis of the oxygen molecule is positioned at an angle to the Fe—O bond (Fig. 7–5a). In contrast, when CO binds to free heme, the Fe, C, and O atoms lie in a straight line (Fig. 7–5b). In both cases, the binding reflects the geometry of hybrid orbitals in each ligand. In myoglobin, His⁶⁴ (His E7), on the O_2-binding side of the heme, is too far away to coordinate with the heme iron, but it does interact with a ligand bound to heme. This residue, called the *distal His*, does not affect the binding of O_2 (Fig. 7–5c) but may preclude the linear binding of CO, providing one explanation for the diminished binding of CO to heme in myoglobin (and hemoglobin). This effect on CO binding is physiologically important, because CO is a low-level byproduct of cellular metabolism. Other factors, not yet well-defined, also seem to modulate the interaction of heme with CO in these proteins.

The binding of O_2 to the heme in myoglobin also depends on molecular motions, or "breathing," in the protein structure. The heme molecule is deeply buried in the folded polypeptide, with no direct path for oxygen to go from the surrounding solution to the ligand-binding site. If the protein were rigid, O_2 could not enter or leave the heme pocket at a measurable rate. However, rapid molecular flexing of the amino acid side chains produces transient cavities in the protein structure, and O_2 evidently makes its way in and out by moving through these cavities. Computer simulations of rapid structural fluctuations in myoglobin suggest that there are many such pathways. One major route is provided by rotation of the side chain of the distal His (His⁶⁴), which occurs on a nanosecond (10^{-9} s) time scale. Even subtle conformational changes can be critical for protein activity.

(a)   **(b)**

figure 7–5
Steric effects on the binding of ligands to the heme of myoglobin. (a) Oxygen binds to heme with the O_2 axis at an angle, a binding conformation readily accommodated by myoglobin. **(b)** Carbon monoxide binds to free heme with the CO axis perpendicular to the plane of the porphyrin ring. CO binding to the heme in myoglobin is forced to adopt a slight angle because the perpendicular arrangement is sterically blocked by His E7, the distal His. This effect weakens the binding of CO to myoglobin. **(c)** Another view showing the arrangement of key amino acid residues around the heme of myoglobin. The bound O_2 is hydrogen-bonded to the distal His, His E7 (His⁶⁴), further facilitating the binding of O_2.

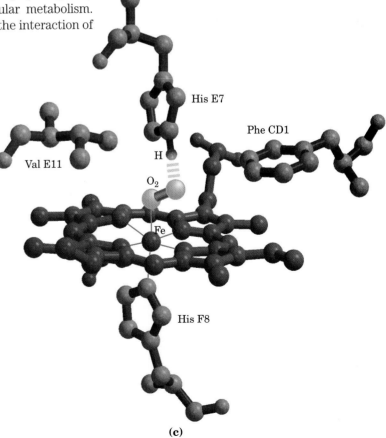

(c)

Oxygen Is Transported in Blood by Hemoglobin

Nearly all the oxygen carried by whole blood in animals is bound and transported by hemoglobin in erythrocytes (red blood cells). Normal human erythrocytes are small (6 to 9 μm in diameter), biconcave disks. They are formed from precursor stem cells called **hemocytoblasts.** In the maturation process, the stem cell produces daughter cells that form large amounts of hemoglobin and then lose their intracellular organelles—nucleus, mitochondria, and endoplasmic reticulum. Erythrocytes are thus incomplete, vestigial cells, unable to reproduce and, in humans, destined to survive for only about 120 days. Their main function is to carry hemoglobin, which is dissolved in the cytosol at a very high concentration (~34% by weight).

In arterial blood passing from the lungs through the heart to the peripheral tissues, hemoglobin is about 96% saturated with oxygen. In the venous blood returning to the heart, hemoglobin is only about 64% saturated. Thus, each 100 mL of blood passing through a tissue releases about one-third of the oxygen it carries, or 6.5 mL of O_2 gas at atmospheric pressure and body temperature.

Myoglobin, with its hyperbolic binding curve for oxygen (Fig. 7–4b), is relatively insensitive to small changes in the concentration of dissolved oxygen and so functions well as an oxygen-storage protein. Hemoglobin, with its multiple subunits and O_2-binding sites, is better suited to oxygen transport. As we will see, interactions between the subunits of a multimeric protein can permit a highly sensitive response to small changes in ligand concentration. Interactions among the subunits in hemoglobin cause conformational changes that alter the affinity of the protein for oxygen. The modulation of oxygen binding allows the O_2-transport protein to respond to changes in oxygen demand by tissues.

Hemoglobin Subunits Are Structurally Similar to Myoglobin

Hemoglobin (M_r 64,500; abbreviated Hb) is roughly spherical, with a diameter of nearly 5.5 nm. It is a tetrameric protein containing four heme prosthetic groups, one associated with each polypeptide chain. Adult hemoglobin contains two types of globin, two α chains (141 residues each) and two β chains (146 residues each). Although fewer than half of the amino acid residues in the polypeptide sequences of the α and β subunits are identical, the three-dimensional structures of the two types of subunits are very similar. Furthermore, their structures are very similar to that of myoglobin (Fig. 7–6), even though the amino acid sequences of the three polypeptides are identical at only 27 positions (Fig. 7–7). All three polypeptides are

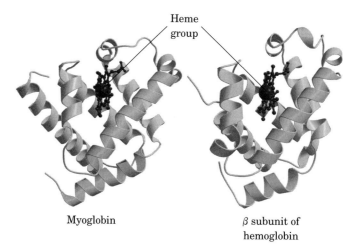

Heme group

Myoglobin

β subunit of hemoglobin

figure 7–6
A comparison of the structures of myoglobin and the β subunit of hemoglobin.

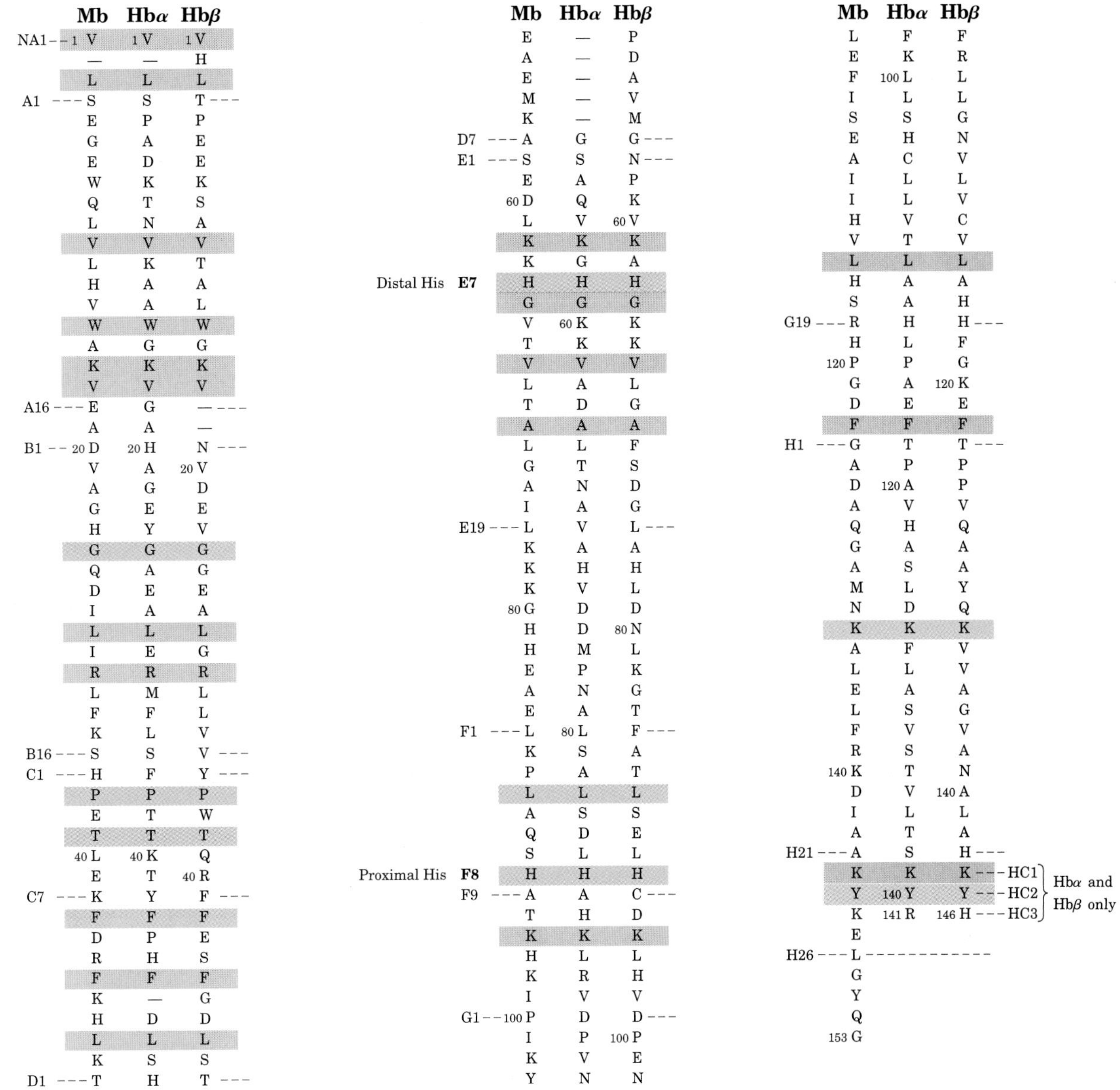

	Mb	Hbα	Hbβ
NA1 -- 1	V	1 V	1 V
	—	—	H
	L	L	L
A1 ---	S	S	T ---
	E	P	P
	G	A	E
	E	D	E
	W	K	K
	Q	T	S
	L	N	A
	V	V	V
	L	K	T
	H	A	A
	V	A	L
	W	W	W
	A	G	G
	K	K	K
	V	V	V
A16 ---	E	G	— ---
	A	A	—
B1 -- 20	D	20 H	N ---
	V	A	20 V
	A	G	D
	G	E	E
	H	Y	V
	G	G	G
	Q	A	E
	D	E	E
	I	A	A
	L	L	L
	I	E	G
	R	R	R
	L	M	L
	F	F	L
	K	L	V
B16 ---	S	S	V ---
C1 ---	H	F	Y ---
	P	P	P
	E	T	W
	T	T	T
40	L	40 K	Q
	E	T	40 R
C7 ---	K	Y	F ---
	F	F	F
	D	P	E
	R	H	S
	F	F	F
	K	—	G
	H	D	D
	L	L	L
	K	S	S
D1 ---	T	H	T ---

	Mb	Hbα	Hbβ
	E	—	P
	A	—	D
	E	—	A
	M	—	V
	K	—	M
D7 ---	A	G	G ---
E1 ---	S	S	N ---
	E	A	P
60	D	Q	K
	L	V	60 V
	K	K	K
	K	G	A
Distal His E7	H	H	H
	G	G	G
	V	60 K	K
	T	K	K
	V	V	V
	L	A	L
	T	D	G
	A	A	A
	L	L	F
	G	T	S
	A	N	D
	I	A	G
E19 ---	L	V	L ---
	K	A	A
	K	H	H
	K	V	L
80	G	D	D
	H	D	80 N
	H	M	L
	E	P	K
	A	N	G
	E	A	T
F1 ---	L	80 L	F ---
	K	S	A
	P	A	T
	L	L	L
	A	S	S
	Q	D	E
	S	L	L
Proximal His F8	H	H	H
F9 ---	A	A	C ---
	T	H	D
	K	K	K
	H	L	L
	K	R	H
	I	V	V
G1 -- 100	P	D	D ---
	I	P	100 P
	K	V	E
	Y	N	N

	Mb	Hbα	Hbβ	
	L	F	F	
	E	K	R	
	F	100 L	L	
	I	L	L	
	S	S	G	
	E	H	N	
	A	C	V	
	I	L	L	
	I	L	V	
	H	V	C	
	V	T	V	
	L	L	L	
	H	A	A	
	S	A	H	
G19 ---	R	H	H ---	
	H	L	F	
120	P	P	G	
	G	A	120 K	
	D	E	E	
	F	F	F	
H1 ---	G	T	T ---	
	A	P	P	
	D	120 A	P	
	A	V	V	
	Q	H	Q	
	G	A	A	
	A	S	A	
	M	L	Y	
	N	D	Q	
	K	K	K	
	A	F	V	
	L	L	V	
	E	A	A	
	L	S	G	
	F	V	V	
	R	S	A	
140	K	T	N	
	D	V	140 A	
	I	L	L	
	A	T	A	
H21 ---	A	S	H ---	
	K	K	K --- HC1	Hbα and Hbβ only
	Y	140 Y	Y --- HC2	
	K	141 R	146 H --- HC3	
	E			
H26 ---	L	-----------		
	G			
	Y			
	Q			
153	G			

figure 7–7

The amino acid sequences of whale myoglobin and the α and β chains of human hemoglobin. Dashed lines mark helix boundaries. To align the sequences optimally, short breaks must be incorporated into both Hb sequences where a few amino acids are present in the other sequences. With the exception of the missing D helix in Hbα, this alignment permits the use of the helix lettering convention that emphasizes the common positioning of amino acid residues that are identical in all three structures (shaded). Residues shaded in red are conserved in all known globins. Note that a common letter-and-number designation for amino acids in two or three different structures does not necessarily correspond to a common position in the linear sequence of amino acids in the polypeptides. For example, the distal His residue is His E7 in all three structures, but corresponds to His[64], His[58], and His[63] in the linear sequences of Mb, Hbα, and Hbβ, respectively. Nonhelical residues at the amino and carboxyl termini, beyond the first (A) and last (H) α-helical segments, are labeled NA and HC, respectively.

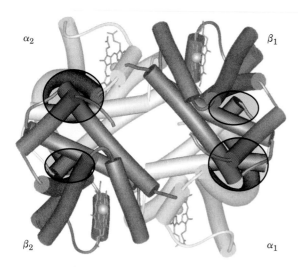

figure 7–8

Dominant interactions between hemoglobin subunits.
In this representation, α subunits are light and β subunits
are dark. The strongest subunit interactions, highlighted,
occur between unlike subunits. When oxygen binds, the
$\alpha_1\beta_1$ contact changes little, but there is a large change at
the $\alpha_1\beta_2$ contact, with several ion pairs broken.

members of the globin family of proteins. The helix-naming convention described for myoglobin is also applied to the hemoglobin polypeptides, except that the α subunit lacks the short D helix. The heme-binding pocket is made up largely of the E and F helices.

The quaternary structure of hemoglobin features strong interactions between unlike subunits. The $\alpha_1\beta_1$ interface (and its $\alpha_2\beta_2$ counterpart) involves over 30 residues and is sufficiently strong that although mild treatment of hemoglobin with urea tends to cause the tetramer to disassemble into αβ dimers, the dimers remain intact. The $\alpha_1\beta_2$ (and $\alpha_2\beta_1$) interface involves 19 residues (Fig. 7–8). Hydrophobic interactions predominate at the interfaces, but there are also many hydrogen bonds and a few ion pairs (sometimes referred to as salt bridges), whose importance is discussed below.

Hemoglobin Undergoes a Structural Change on Binding Oxygen

X-ray analysis has revealed two major conformations of hemoglobin: the **R state** and the **T state.** Although oxygen binds to hemoglobin in either state, it has a significantly higher affinity for hemoglobin in the R state. Oxygen binding stabilizes the R state. When oxygen is absent experimentally, the T state is more stable and is thus the predominant conformation of **deoxyhemoglobin.** T and R originally denoted "tense" and "relaxed," respectively, because the T state is stabilized by a greater number of ion pairs, many of which lie at the $\alpha_1\beta_2$ (and $\alpha_2\beta_1$) interface (Fig. 7–9). The binding

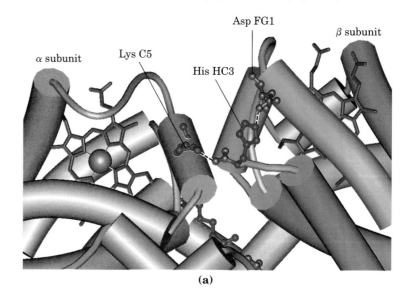

figure 7–9

Some ion pairs that stabilize the T state of deoxyhemoglobin. (a) A close-up view of a portion of a deoxyhemoglobin molecule in the T state. Interactions between the ion pairs His HC3 and Asp FG1 of the β subunit (blue) and between Lys C5 of the α subunit (gray) and the α-carboxyl group of His HC3 of the β subunit are shown with dashed lines. (Recall that HC3 is the carboxyl-terminal residue of the β subunit.) **(b)** The interactions between these ion pairs and others not shown in **(a)** are schematized in this representation of the extended polypeptide chains of hemoglobin.

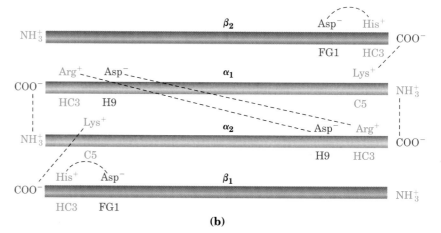

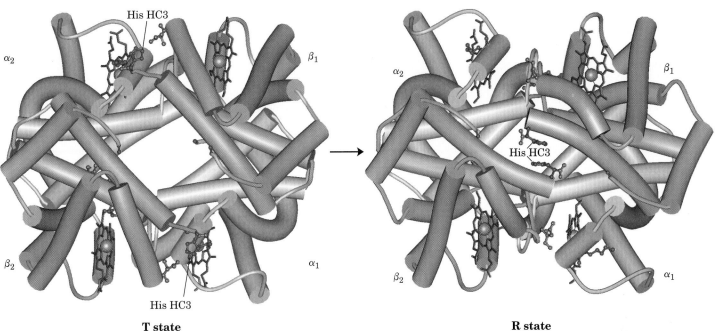

T state   **R state**

figure 7–10
The T ⟶ R transition. In these depictions of deoxy-hemoglobin, as in Figure 7–9, the β subunits are light blue and the α subunits are gray. Positively charged side chains and chain termini involved in ion pairs are shown in blue, their negatively charged partners in pink. The Lys C5 of each α subunit and Asp FG1 of each β subunit are visible but not labeled (compare Fig. 7–9a). Note that the molecule is oriented slightly differently than in Figure 7–9. The transition from the T state to the R state shifts the subunit pairs substantially, affecting certain ion pairs. Most noticeably, the His HC3 residues at the carboxyl termini of the β subunits, which are involved in ion pairs in the T state, rotate in the R state toward the center of the molecule where they are no longer in ion pairs. Another dramatic result of the T ⟶ R transition is a narrowing of the pocket between the β subunits.

of O₂ to a hemoglobin subunit in the T state triggers a change in conformation to the R state. When the entire protein undergoes this transition, the structures of the individual subunits change little, but the αβ subunit pairs slide past each other and rotate, narrowing the pocket between the β subunits (Fig. 7–10). In this process, some of the ion pairs that stabilize the T state are broken and some new ones are formed.

   Max Perutz proposed that the T ⟶ R transition is triggered by changes in the positions of key amino acid side chains surrounding the heme. In the T state, the porphyrin is slightly puckered, causing the heme iron to protrude somewhat on the proximal His (His F8) side. The binding of O₂ causes the heme to assume a more planar conformation, shifting the position of the proximal His and the attached F helix (Fig. 7–11). Also, a Val residue in the E helix (Val E11) partially blocks the heme in the T state and must swing out of the way for oxygen to bind (Fig. 7–10). These changes lead to adjustments in the ion pairs at the α₁β₂ interface.

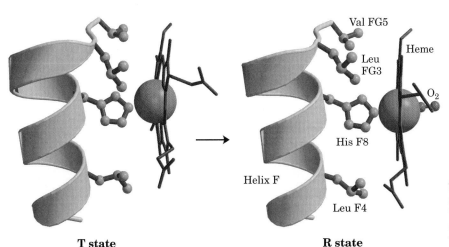

T state   **R state**

figure 7–11
Changes in conformation near heme on O₂ binding. The shift in the position of the F helix when heme binds O₂ is one of the adjustments that is believed to trigger the T ⟶ R transition.

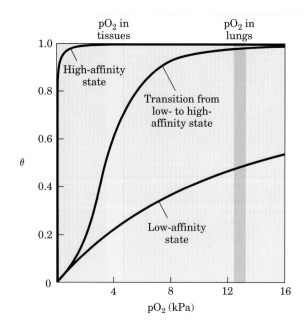

figure 7–12

A sigmoid (cooperative) binding curve. A sigmoid binding curve can be viewed as a hybrid curve reflecting a transition from a low-affinity to a high-affinity state. Cooperative binding, as manifested by a sigmoid binding curve, renders hemoglobin more sensitive to the small differences in O_2 concentration between the tissues and the lungs, allowing hemoglobin to bind oxygen in the lungs where pO_2 is high and release it in the tissues where pO_2 is low.

Hemoglobin Binds Oxygen Cooperatively

Hemoglobin must bind oxygen efficiently in the lungs, where the pO_2 is about 13.3 kPa, and release oxygen in the tissues, where the pO_2 is about 4 kPa. Myoglobin, or any protein that binds oxygen with a hyperbolic binding curve, would be ill-suited to this function, for the reason illustrated in Figure 7–12. A protein that bound O_2 with high affinity would bind it efficiently in the lungs but would not release much of it in the tissues. If the protein bound oxygen with a sufficiently low affinity to release it in the tissues, it would not pick up much oxygen in the lungs.

Hemoglobin solves the problem by undergoing a transition from a low-affinity state (the T state) to a high-affinity state (the R state) as more O_2 molecules are bound. As a result, hemoglobin has a hybrid S-shaped, or sigmoid, binding curve for oxygen (Fig. 7–12). A single-subunit protein with a single ligand-binding site cannot produce a sigmoid binding curve—even if binding elicits a conformational change—because each molecule of ligand binds independently and cannot affect the binding of another molecule. In contrast, O_2 binding to individual subunits of hemoglobin can alter the affinity for O_2 in adjacent subunits. The first molecule of O_2 that interacts with deoxyhemoglobin binds weakly, because it binds to a subunit in the T state. Its binding, however, leads to conformational changes that are communicated to adjacent subunits, making it easier for additional molecules of O_2 to bind. In effect, the T $\longrightarrow$ R transition occurs more readily in the second subunit once O_2 is bound to the first subunit. The last (fourth) O_2 molecule binds to a heme in a subunit that is already in the R state, and hence it binds with much higher affinity than the first molecule.

An **allosteric protein** is one in which the binding of a ligand to one site affects the binding properties of another site on the same protein. The term allosteric derives from the Greek *allos*, "other," and *stereos*, "solid" or "shape." Allosteric proteins are those having "other shapes" or conformations induced by the binding of ligands referred to as modulators. The conformational changes induced by the modulator(s) interconvert more-active and less-active forms of the protein. The modulators for allosteric proteins may be either inhibitors or activators. When the normal ligand and modulator are identical, the interaction is termed **homotropic.** When the modulator is a molecule other than the normal ligand the interaction is **heterotropic.** Some proteins have two or more modulators and therefore can have both homotropic and heterotropic interactions.

Cooperative binding of a ligand to a multimeric protein, such as we observe with the binding of O_2 to hemoglobin, is a form of allosteric binding often observed in multimeric proteins. The binding of one ligand affects the affinities of any remaining unfilled binding sites, and O_2 can be considered as both a normal ligand and an activating homotropic modulator. There is only one binding site for O_2 on each subunit, so the allosteric effects giving rise to cooperativity are mediated by conformational changes transmitted from one subunit to another by subunit-subunit interactions. A sigmoid bonding curve is diagnostic of cooperative binding. It permits a much more sensitive response to ligand concentration and is important to the function of many multisubunit proteins. The principle of allostery extends readily to regulatory enzymes, as we will see in Chapter 8.

Cooperative Ligand Binding Can Be Described Quantitatively

Cooperative binding of oxygen by hemoglobin was first analyzed by Archibald Hill in 1910. For a protein with n binding sites, the equilibrium of Equation 7–1 becomes

$$P + nL \rightleftharpoons PL_n \qquad (7-12)$$

and the expression for the association constant becomes

$$K_a = \frac{[PL_n]}{[P][L]^n} \qquad (7-13)$$

The expression for θ (see Eqn 7–8) is

$$\theta = \frac{[L]^n}{[L]^n + K_d} \qquad (7-14)$$

Rearranging, then taking the log of both sides, yields

$$\frac{\theta}{1 - \theta} = \frac{[L]^n}{K_d} \qquad (7-15)$$

$$\log\left(\frac{\theta}{1 - \theta}\right) = n \log [L] - \log K_d \qquad (7-16)$$

Equation 7–16 is the **Hill equation,** and a plot of $\log [\theta/(1 - \theta)]$ versus $\log$ [L] is called a **Hill plot.** Based on the equation, the Hill plot should have a slope of n. However, the experimentally determined slope actually reflects not the number of binding sites, but the degree of interaction between them. The slope of a Hill plot is therefore denoted n_H, the **Hill coefficient,** which is a measure of the degree of cooperativity. If n_H equals 1, ligand binding is not cooperative, a situation that can arise even in a multisubunit protein if the subunits do not communicate. An n_H of greater than 1 indicates positive cooperativity in ligand binding. This is the situation observed in hemoglobin, in which the binding of one molecule of ligand facilitates the binding of others. The theoretical upper limit for n_H is reached when $n_H = n$. In this case the binding would be completely cooperative: all binding sites on the protein would bind ligand simultaneously, and no protein molecules partially saturated with ligand would be present under any conditions. This limit is never reached in practice, and the measured value of n_H is always less than the actual number of ligand-binding sites in the protein.

An n_H of less than 1 indicates negative cooperativity, in which the binding of one molecule of ligand *impedes* the binding of others. Well-documented cases of negative cooperativity are rare.

To adapt the Hill equation to the binding of oxygen to hemoglobin we must again substitute pO_2 for [L] and P_{50} for K_d:

$$\log\left(\frac{\theta}{1 - \theta}\right) = n \log pO_2 - \log P_{50} \qquad (7-17)$$

Hill plots for myoglobin and hemoglobin are given in Figure 7–13.

Two Models Suggest Mechanisms for Cooperative Binding

Biochemists now know a great deal about the T and R states of hemoglobin, but much remains to be learned about how the T $\longrightarrow$ R transition occurs. Two models for the cooperative binding of ligands to proteins with multiple binding sites have greatly influenced thinking about this problem.

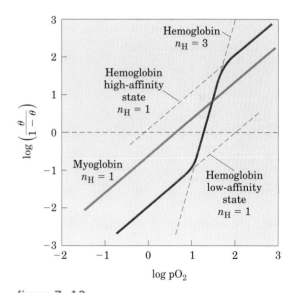

figure 7–13
Hill plots for the binding of oxygen to myoglobin and hemoglobin. When $n_H = 1$, there is no evident cooperativity. The maximum degree of cooperativity observed for hemoglobin corresponds approximately to $n_H = 3$. Note that while this indicates a high level of cooperativity, n_H is less than n, the number of O_2-binding sites in hemoglobin. This is normal for a protein that exhibits allosteric binding behavior.

figure 7–14
Two general models for the interconversion of inactive and active forms of cooperative ligand-binding proteins. Although the models may be applied to any protein—including any enzyme (Chapter 8)—that exhibits cooperative binding, four subunits are shown because the model was originally proposed for hemoglobin. In the concerted, or all-or-none, model **(a)** all the subunits are postulated to be in the same conformation, either all ○ (low affinity or inactive) or all □ (high affinity or active). Depending on the equilibrium, K_1, between ○ and □ forms, the binding of one or more ligand molecules (L) will pull the equilibrium toward the □ form. Subunits with bound L are shaded. In the sequential model **(b)** each individual subunit can be in either the ○ or □ form. A very large number of conformations is thus possible.

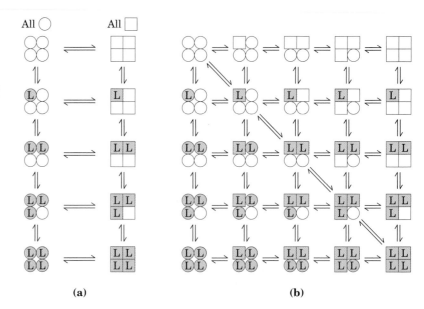

(a)   (b)

The first model was proposed by Jacques Monod, Jeffries Wyman, and Jean-Pierre Changeux in 1965, and is called the **MWC model** or the **concerted model** (Fig. 7–14a). The concerted model assumes that the subunits of a cooperatively binding protein are functionally identical, that each subunit can exist in (at least) two conformations, and that all subunits undergo the transition from one conformation to the other simultaneously. In this model, no protein has individual subunits in different conformations. The two conformations are in equilibrium. The ligand can bind to either conformation, but binds each with different affinity. Successive binding of ligand molecules to the low-affinity conformation (which is more stable in the absence of ligand) makes a transition to the high-affinity conformation more likely.

In the second model, the **sequential model** (Fig. 7–14b), proposed in 1966 by Daniel Koshland and colleagues, ligand binding can induce a change of conformation in an individual subunit. A conformational change in one subunit makes a similar change in an adjacent subunit, as well as the binding of a second ligand molecule, more likely. There are more potential intermediate states in this model than in the concerted model. The two models are not mutually exclusive; the concerted model may be viewed as the "all-or-none" limiting case of the sequential model. In Chapter 8 we will use these models when we investigate allosteric enzymes.

Hemoglobin Also Transports H$^+$ and CO$_2$

In addition to carrying nearly all the oxygen required by cells from the lungs to the tissues, hemoglobin carries two end products of cellular respiration—H$^+$ and CO$_2$—from the tissues to the lungs and the kidneys, where they are excreted. The CO$_2$, produced by oxidation of organic fuels in mitochondria, is hydrated to form bicarbonate:

$$CO_2 + H_2O \rightleftharpoons H^+ + HCO_3^-$$

This reaction is catalyzed by **carbonic anhydrase,** an enzyme particularly abundant in erythrocytes. Carbon dioxide is not very soluble in aqueous solution, and bubbles of CO$_2$ would form in the tissues and blood if it were not converted to bicarbonate. As you can see from the equation, the hydration of CO$_2$ results in an increase in the H$^+$ concentration (a decrease in pH) in the tissues. The binding of oxygen by hemoglobin is profoundly influenced by pH and CO_2 concentration, so the interconversion of CO_2 and bicarbonate is of great importance to the regulation of oxygen binding and release in the blood.

Hemoglobin transports about 20% of the total H^+ and CO_2 formed in the tissues to the lungs and the kidneys. The binding of H^+ and CO_2 is inversely related to the binding of oxygen. At the relatively low pH and high CO_2 concentration of peripheral tissues, the affinity of hemoglobin for oxygen decreases as H^+ and CO_2 are bound, and O_2 is released to the tissues. Conversely, in the capillaries of the lung, as CO_2 is excreted and the blood pH consequently rises, the affinity of hemoglobin for oxygen increases and the protein binds more O_2 for transport to the peripheral tissues. This effect of pH and CO_2 concentration on the binding and release of oxygen by hemoglobin is called the **Bohr effect,** after Christian Bohr, the Danish physiologist (and father of physicist Niels Bohr) who discovered it in 1904.

The binding equilibrium for hemoglobin and one molecule of oxygen can be designated by the reaction

$$Hb + O_2 \rightleftharpoons HbO_2$$

but this is not a complete statement. To account for the effect of H^+ concentration on this binding equilibrium, we rewrite the reaction as

$$HHb^+ + O_2 \rightleftharpoons HbO_2 + H^+$$

where HHb^+ denotes a protonated form of hemoglobin. This equation tells us that the O_2-saturation curve of hemoglobin is influenced by the H^+ concentration (Fig. 7–15). Both O_2 and H^+ are bound by hemoglobin, but with inverse affinity. When the oxygen concentration is high, as in the lungs, hemoglobin binds O_2 and releases protons. When the oxygen concentration is low, as in the peripheral tissues, H^+ is bound and O_2 is released.

Oxygen and H^+ are not bound at the same sites in hemoglobin. Oxygen binds to the iron atoms of the hemes, whereas H^+ binds to any of several amino acid residues in the protein. A major contribution to the Bohr effect is made by His^{146} (His HC3) of the β subunits. When protonated, this residue forms one of the ion pairs—to Asp^{94} (Asp FG1)—that helps stabilize deoxyhemoglobin in the T state (Fig. 7–9). The ion pair stabilizes the protonated form of His HC3, giving this residue an abnormally high pK_a in the T state. The pK_a falls to its normal value of 6.0 in the R state because the ion pair cannot form, and this residue is largely unprotonated in oxyhemoglobin at pH 7.6, the blood pH in the lungs. As the concentration of H^+ rises, protonation of His HC3 promotes release of oxygen by favoring a transition to the T state. Protonation of the amino-terminal residues of the α subunits, certain other His residues, and perhaps other groups has a similar effect.

Thus we see that the four polypeptide chains of hemoglobin communicate with each other not only about O_2 binding to their heme groups, but also about H^+ binding to specific amino acid residues. And there is still more to the story. Hemoglobin also binds CO_2, again in a manner inversely related to the binding of oxygen. Carbon dioxide binds as a carbamate group to the α-amino group at the amino-terminal end of each globin chain, forming carbaminohemoglobin:

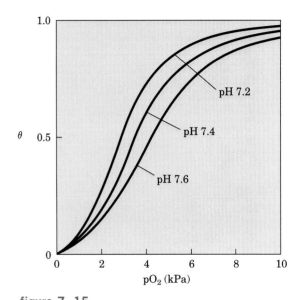

figure 7–15
Effect of pH on the binding of oxygen to hemoglobin.
The pH of blood is 7.6 in the lungs and 7.2 in the tissues. Experimental measurements on hemoglobin binding are often performed at pH 7.4.

This reaction produces H^+, contributing to the Bohr effect. The bound carbamates also form additional salt bridges (not shown in Fig. 7–9) that help to stabilize the T state and promote the release of oxygen.

When the concentration of carbon dioxide is high, as in peripheral tissues, some CO_2 binds to hemoglobin and the affinity for O_2 decreases, causing its release. Conversely, when hemoglobin reaches the lungs, the high oxygen concentration promotes binding of O_2 and release of CO_2. It is the capacity to communicate ligand-binding information from one polypeptide subunit to the others that makes the hemoglobin molecule so beautifully adapted to integrating the transport of O_2, CO_2, and H^+ by erythrocytes.

Oxygen Binding to Hemoglobin Is Regulated by 2,3-Bisphosphoglycerate

The interaction of **2,3-bisphosphoglycerate** (BPG) with hemoglobin provides an example of heterotropic allosteric modulation. BPG is present in relatively high concentrations in erythrocytes. When hemoglobin is isolated, it contains substantial amounts of bound BPG, which can be difficult to remove completely. In fact, the O_2-binding curves for hemoglobin that we have examined to this point were obtained in the presence of bound BPG. 2,3-Bisphosphoglycerate is known to greatly reduce the affinity of hemoglobin for oxygen—there is an inverse relationship between the binding of O_2 and the binding of BPG. We can therefore describe another binding process for hemoglobin:

$$HbBPG + O_2 \rightleftharpoons HbO_2 + BPG$$

BPG binds at a site distant from the oxygen-binding site and regulates the O_2-binding affinity of hemoglobin in relation to the pO_2 in the lungs. BPG plays an important role in the physiological adaptation to the lower pO_2 available at high altitudes. For a healthy human strolling by the ocean, the binding of O_2 to hemoglobin is regulated such that the amount of O_2 delivered to the tissues is equivalent to nearly 40% of the maximum that could be carried by the blood (Fig. 7–16). If the same person is quickly transported to a mountainside at an altitude of 4,500 meters, where the pO_2 is considerably lower, the delivery of O_2 to the tissues is reduced. However,

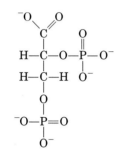

2,3-Bisphosphoglycerate

figure 7–16

Effect of BPG on the binding of oxygen to hemoglobin. The BPG concentration in normal human blood is about 5 mM at sea level and about 8 mM at high altitudes. Note that hemoglobin binds to oxygen quite tightly when BPG is entirely absent, and the binding curve appears to be hyperbolic. In reality, the measured Hill coefficient for O_2-binding cooperativity decreases only slightly (from 3 to about 2.5) when BPG is removed from hemoglobin, but the rising part of the sigmoid curve is confined to a very small region close to the origin. At sea level, hemoglobin is nearly saturated with O_2 in the lungs, but only 60% saturated in the tissues, so that the amount of oxygen released in the tissues is close to 40% of the maximum that can be carried in the blood. At high altitudes, O_2 delivery declines by about one-fourth, to 30% of maximum. An increase in BPG concentration, however, decreases the affinity of hemoglobin for O_2 so that nearly 40% of what can be carried is again delivered to the tissues.

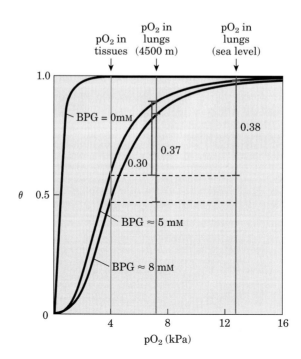

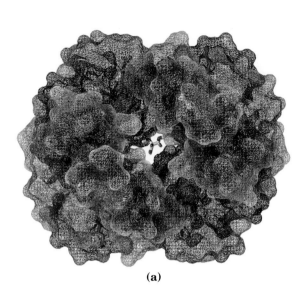

(a)

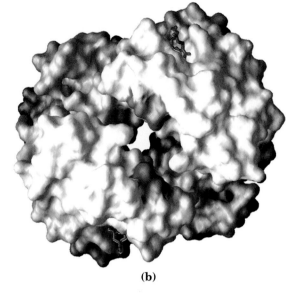

(b)

after just a few hours at the higher altitude, the BPG concentration in the blood has begun to rise, leading to a decrease in the affinity of hemoglobin for oxygen. This adjustment in the BPG level has only a small effect on the binding of O_2 in the lungs but a considerable effect on the release of O_2 in the tissues. As a result, the delivery of oxygen to the tissues is restored to nearly 40% of that which can be transported by the blood. The situation is reversed when the person returns to sea level. The BPG concentration in erythrocytes also increases in people suffering from **hypoxia,** lowered oxygenation of peripheral tissues due to inadequate function of the lungs or circulatory system.

BPG binds to hemoglobin in the cavity between the β subunits in the T state (Fig. 7–17). This cavity is lined with positively charged amino acid residues that interact with the negatively charged groups of BPG. Unlike O_2, only one molecule of BPG is bound to each hemoglobin tetramer. BPG lowers hemoglobin's affinity for oxygen by stabilizing the T state. The transition to the R state narrows the binding pocket for BPG, precluding BPG binding. In the absence of BPG, hemoglobin is converted to the R state more easily.

Regulation of oxygen binding to hemoglobin by BPG has an important role in fetal development. Because a fetus must extract oxygen from its mother's blood, fetal hemoglobin must have greater affinity than the maternal hemoglobin for O_2. In fetuses, γ subunits are synthesized rather than β subunits, and $\alpha_2\gamma_2$ hemoglobin is formed. This tetramer has a much lower affinity for BPG than normal adult hemoglobin, and a correspondingly higher affinity for O_2.

Sickle-Cell Anemia Is a Molecular Disease of Hemoglobin

The great importance of the amino acid sequence in determining the secondary, tertiary, and quaternary structures of globular proteins, and thus their biological functions, is strikingly demonstrated by the hereditary human disease sickle-cell anemia. More than 300 genetic variants of hemoglobin are known to occur in the human population. Most of these variations consist of differences in a single amino acid residue. The effects on hemoglobin structure and function are often minor but can sometimes be extraordinary. Each hemoglobin variation is the product of an altered gene. The variant genes are called alleles. Because humans generally have two copies of each gene, an individual may have two copies of one allele (thus being homozygous for that gene) or one copy of each of two different alleles

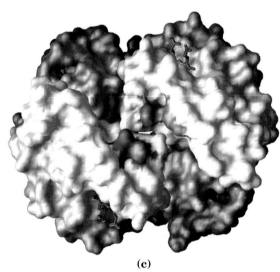

(c)

figure 7–17

Binding of BPG to deoxyhemoglobin. (a) BPG binding stabilizes the T state of deoxyhemoglobin, shown here as a mesh surface image. **(b)** The negative charges of BPG interact with several positively charged groups (shown in blue in this GRASP surface image) that surround the pocket between the β subunits in the T state. **(c)** The binding pocket for BPG disappears on oxygenation, following transition to the R state. (Compare **(b)** and **(c)** with Fig. 7–10.)

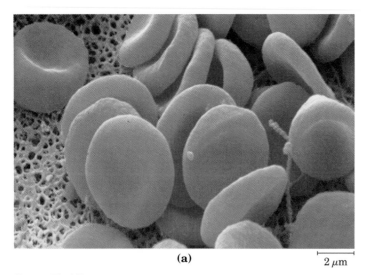

(a)   2 μm   (b)

figure 7–18

A comparison of uniform, cup-shaped, normal erythrocytes **(a)** with the variably shaped erythrocytes seen in
sickle-cell anemia **(b).** These cells range from normal to
spiny or sickle-shaped.

(heterozygous). Sickle-cell anemia is a genetic disease in which an individual
has inherited the allele for sickle-cell hemoglobin from both parents. The
erythrocytes of these individuals are fewer and also abnormal. In addition
to an unusually large number of immature cells, the blood contains many
long, thin, crescent-shaped erythrocytes that look like the blade of a sickle
(Fig. 7–18). When hemoglobin from sickle cells (called hemoglobin S) is deoxygenated, it becomes insoluble and forms polymers that aggregate into
tubular fibers (Fig. 7–19). Normal hemoglobin (hemoglobin A) remains sol-

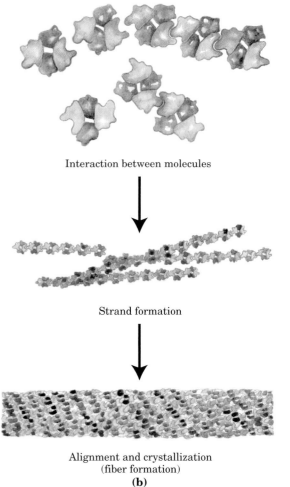

Interaction between molecules

↓

Strand formation

↓

Alignment and crystallization
(fiber formation)
(b)

figure 7–19

Normal and sickle-cell hemoglobin. (a) Subtle differences between the conformations of hemoglobin A and
hemoglobin S result from a single amino acid change in
the β chains. **(b)** As a result of this change, deoxyhemoglobin S has a hydrophobic patch on its surface, which
causes the molecules to aggregate into strands that align
into insoluble fibers.

Hemoglobin A   Hemoglobin S

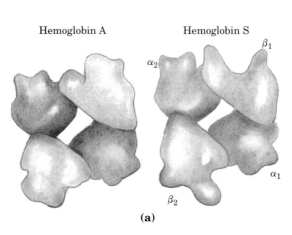

β_1

α_2

α_1

β_2

(a)

uble on deoxygenation. The insoluble fibers of deoxygenated hemoglobin S are responsible for the deformed sickle shape of the erythrocytes, and the proportion of sickled cells increases greatly as blood is deoxygenated.

The altered properties of hemoglobin S result from a single amino acid substitution, a Val instead of a Glu residue at position 6 in the two β chains. The R group of valine has no electric charge, whereas glutamate has a negative charge at pH 7.4. Hemoglobin S therefore has two fewer negative charges than hemoglobin A, one for each of the two β chains. Replacement of the Glu residue by Val creates a "sticky" hydrophobic contact point at position 6 of the β chain, which is on the outer surface of the molecule. These sticky spots cause deoxyhemoglobin S molecules to associate abnormally with each other, forming the long, fibrous aggregates characteristic of this disorder.

Sickle-cell anemia occurs in individuals homozygous for the sickle-cell allele of the gene encoding the β subunit of hemoglobin. Individuals who receive the sickle-cell allele from only one parent and are thus heterozygous experience a milder condition called sickle-cell trait; only about 1% of their erythrocytes become sickled on deoxygenation. These individuals may live completely normal lives if they avoid vigorous exercise or other stresses on the circulatory system.

People with sickle-cell anemia suffer from repeated crises brought on by physical exertion. They become weak, dizzy, and short of breath, and they also experience heart murmurs and an increased pulse rate. The hemoglobin content of their blood is only about half the normal value of 15 to 16 g/100 mL because sickled cells are very fragile and rupture easily; this results in anemia ("lack of blood"). An even more serious consequence is that capillaries become blocked by the long, abnormally shaped cells, causing severe pain and interfering with normal organ function—a major factor in the early death of many people with the disease.

Without medical treatment, people with sickle-cell anemia usually die in childhood. Nevertheless, the sickle-cell allele is surprisingly common in certain parts of Africa. Investigation into the persistence of an allele that is so obviously deleterious in homozygous individuals led to the finding that the allele confers a small but significant resistance to lethal forms of malaria in heterozygous individuals. Natural selection has resulted in an allele population that balances the deleterious effects of the homozygous condition against the resistance to malaria afforded by the heterozygous condition.

Complementary Interactions between Proteins and Ligands: The Immune System and Immunoglobulins

Our discussion of oxygen-binding proteins showed how the conformations of these proteins affect and are affected by the binding of small ligands (O_2 or CO) to the heme group. However, most protein-ligand interactions do not involve a prosthetic group. Instead, the binding site for a ligand is more often like the hemoglobin binding site for BPG—a cleft in the protein lined with amino acid residues, arranged to render the binding interaction highly specific. Effective discrimination between ligands is the norm at binding sites, even when the ligands have only minor structural differences.

All vertebrates have an immune system capable of distinguishing molecular "self" from "nonself" and then destroying those entities identified as nonself. In this way, the immune system eliminates viruses, bacteria, and other pathogens and molecules that may pose a threat to the organism. On a physiological level, the response of the immune system to an invader is an intricate and coordinated set of interactions among many classes of proteins, molecules, and cell types. However, at the level of individual proteins, the immune response demonstrates how an acutely sensitive and specific biochemical system is built upon the reversible binding of ligands to proteins.

The Immune Response Features a Specialized Array of Cells and Proteins

Immunity is brought about by a variety of **leukocytes** (white blood cells), including **macrophages** and **lymphocytes,** all arising from undifferentiated stem cells in the bone marrow. Leukocytes can leave the bloodstream and patrol the tissues, each cell producing one or more proteins capable of recognizing and binding to molecules that might signal an infection.

The immune response consists of two complementary systems, the humoral and cellular immune systems. The **humoral immune system** (Latin *humor,* "fluid") is directed at bacterial infections and extracellular viruses (those found in the body fluids), but can also respond to individual proteins introduced into the organism. The **cellular immune system** destroys host cells infected by viruses and also destroys some parasites and foreign tissues.

The proteins at the heart of the humoral immune response are soluble proteins called **antibodies** or **immunoglobulins,** often abbreviated Ig. Immunoglobulins bind bacteria, viruses, or large molecules identified as foreign and target them for destruction. Making up 20% of blood protein, the immunoglobulins are produced by **B lymphocytes** or **B cells,** so named because they complete their development in the *b*one marrow.

The agents at the heart of the cellular immune response are a class of **T lymphocytes** or **T cells** (so called because the latter stages of their development occur in the *t*hymus) known as **cytotoxic T cells (T_C cells,** also called killer T cells). Recognition of infected cells or parasites involves proteins called **T-cell receptors** on the surface of T_C cells. Receptors are proteins, usually found on the outer surface of cells and extending through the plasma membrane; they recognize and bind extracellular ligands, triggering changes inside the cell.

In addition to cytotoxic T cells, there are **helper T cells (T_H cells),** whose function it is to produce soluble signaling proteins called cytokines, which include the interleukins. T_H cells interact with macrophages. Table 7–2 summarizes the functions of the various leukocytes of the immune system.

Each recognition protein of the immune system, either an antibody produced by a B cell or a receptor on the surface of a T cell, specifically binds some particular chemical structure, distinguishing it from virtually all others. Humans are capable of producing over 10^8 different antibodies with distinct binding specificities. This extraordinary diversity makes it likely that any chemical structure on the surface of a virus or invading cell will be recognized and bound by one or more antibodies. Antibody diversity is derived from random reassembly of a set of immunoglobulin gene segments via genetic recombination mechanisms.

Some properties of the interactions between antibodies or T-cell receptors and the molecules they bind are unique to the immune system, and a specialized lexicon is used to describe them. Any molecule or pathogen capable of eliciting an immune response is called an **antigen.** An antigen may be a virus, a bacterial cell wall, or an individual protein or other macromolecule. A complex antigen may be bound by a number of different antibodies. An individual antibody or T-cell receptor binds only a particular molecular structure within the antigen, called its **antigenic determinant** or **epitope.**

It would be unproductive for the immune system to respond to small molecules that are common intermediates and products of cellular metabolism. Molecules of $M_r < 5,000$ are generally not antigenic. However, small molecules can be covalently attached to large proteins in the laboratory, and in this

table 7–2

Some Types of Leukocytes Associated with the Immune System

Cell type	Function
Macrophages	Ingest large particles and cells by phagocytosis
B lymphocytes (B cells)	Produce and secrete antibodies
T lymphocytes (T cells)	
Cytotoxic (killer) T cells (T_C)	Interact with infected host cells through receptors on T-cell surface
Helper T cells (T_H)	Interact with macrophages and secrete cytokines (interleukins) that stimulate T_C, T_H, and B cells to proliferate.

form they may elicit an immune response. These small molecules are called **haptens.** The antibodies produced in response to protein-linked haptens will then bind to the same small molecules when they are free. Such antibodies are sometimes used in the development of analytical tests described later in this chapter.

The interactions of antibody and antigen are much better understood than are the binding properties of T-cell receptors. However, before focusing on antibodies, we need to look at the humoral and cellular immune systems in more detail to put the fundamental biochemical interactions into their proper context.

Self Is Distinguished from Nonself by the Display of Peptides on Cell Surfaces

The immune system must identify and destroy pathogens, but it must also recognize and *not* destroy the normal proteins and cells of the host organism—the "self." Detection of protein antigens in the host is mediated by **MHC (major histocompatibility complex) proteins.** MHC proteins bind peptide fragments of proteins digested in the cell and present them on the outside surface of the cell. These peptides normally come from the digestion of typical cellular proteins, but during a viral infection viral proteins are also digested and presented by MHC proteins. Peptide fragments from foreign proteins that are displayed by MHC proteins are the antigens the immune system recognizes as nonself. T-cell receptors bind these fragments and launch the subsequent steps of the immune response. There are two classes of MHC proteins (Fig. 7–20), which differ in their distribution among cell types and in the source of digested proteins whose peptides they display.

figure 7–20

MHC proteins These proteins consist of α and β chains. In class I MHC proteins **(a),** the small β chain is invariant but the amino acid sequence of the α chain exhibits a high degree of variability, localized in specific domains of the protein that appear on the outside of the cell. Each human produces up to six different α chains for class 1 MHC proteins. In class II MHC proteins **(b),** both the α and β chains have regions of relatively high variability near their amino-terminal ends.

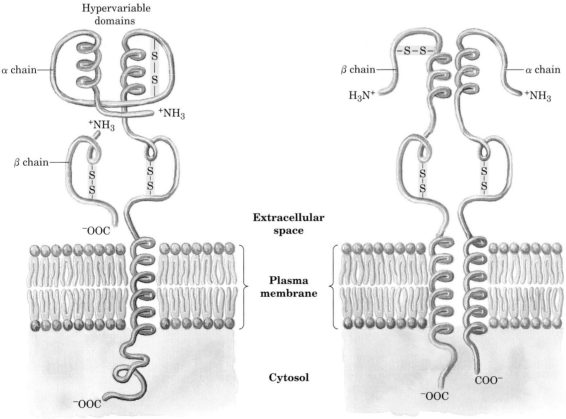

(a) Class I MHC protein   (b) Class II MHC protein

Class I MHC proteins (Fig. 7–21) are found on the surface of virtually all vertebrate cells. There are countless variants in the human population, placing them among the most polymorphic of proteins. Because individuals produce up to six class I MHC protein variants, any two individuals are unlikely to have the same set. Class I MHC proteins bind and display peptides derived from the proteolytic degradation and turnover of proteins that occurs randomly within the cell. These complexes of peptides and class I MHC proteins are the recognition targets of the T-cell receptors of the T_C cells in the cellular immune system. The general pattern of immune system recognition was first described by Rolf Zinkernagel and Peter Doherty in 1974.

Each T_C cell has many copies of only one T-cell receptor that is specific for a particular class I MHC protein–peptide complex. To avoid creating a

figure 7–21
Structure of a human class I MHC protein. (a) This image is derived in part from the determined structure of the extracellular portion of the protein. The α chain of MHC is shown in gray; the small β chain is blue; the disulfide bonds are yellow. A bound ligand, a peptide derived from HIV, is shown in red. **(b)** Top view showing a surface contour image of the site where peptides are bound and displayed. The HIV peptide (red) occupies the site. This part of the class I MHC protein interacts with T-cell receptors.

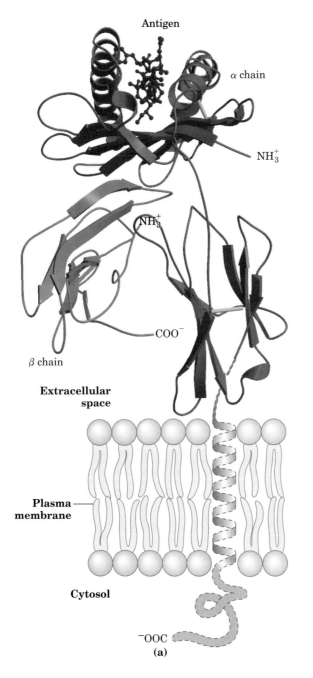

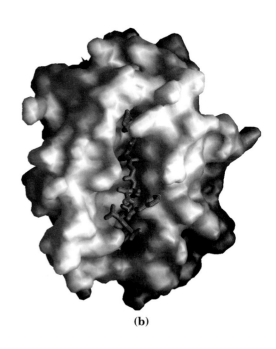

(b)

legion of T_C cells that would set upon and destroy normal cells, the maturation of T_C cells in the thymus includes a stringent selection process that eliminates more than 95% of the developing T_C cells, including those that might recognize and bind class I MHC proteins displaying peptides from cellular proteins of the organism itself. The T_C cells that survive and mature are those with T-cell receptors that do not bind to the organism's own proteins. The result is a population of cells that bind foreign peptides bound to class I MHC proteins of the host cell. These binding interactions lead to the destruction of parasites and virus-infected cells. When an organ is transplanted, its foreign class I MHC proteins are also bound by T_C cells, leading to tissue rejection.

Class II MHC proteins occur on the surfaces of a few types of specialized cells that take up foreign antigens, including macrophages and B lymphocytes. Like class I MHC proteins, the class II proteins are highly polymorphic, with many variants in the human population. Each human is capable of producing up to 12 variants, and thus it is unlikely that any two individuals have an identical set of variants. The class II MHC proteins bind and display peptides derived not from cellular proteins but from external proteins ingested by the cells. The resulting class II MHC protein–peptide complexes are the binding targets of the T-cell receptors of the various helper T cells. T_H cells, like T_C cells, undergo a stringent selection process in the thymus, eliminating those that recognize the individual's own cellular proteins.

Despite the elimination of most T_C and T_H cells during the selection process in the thymus, a very large number survive, and these provide the immune response. Each survivor has a single type of T-cell receptor that can bind to one particular chemical structure. The T cells patrolling the bloodstream and the tissues carry millions of different binding specificities in the T-cell receptors. Within the highly varied T-cell population there is almost always a contingent of cells that can specifically bind any antigen that might appear. The vast majority of these cells never encounter a foreign antigen to which they can bind and typically die within a few days, replaced by new generations of T cells endlessly patrolling in search of the interaction that will launch the full immune response.

Molecular Interactions at Cell Surfaces Trigger the Immune Response

A new antigen is often the harbinger of an infection—a signal to the immune system that a virus or other parasite may be rapidly growing in the organism. Those few T cells and B cells possessing receptors or antibodies that can bind the antigen must be rapidly and selectively propagated to eliminate the infection. A hypothetical viral infection illustrates how this occurs.

When a virus invades a cell, it makes use of cellular functions and resources to replicate its nucleic acid and make viral proteins. Once inside the cell, viral macromolecules are relatively inaccessible to the antibodies of the humoral immune system. However, some of the class I MHC proteins that find their way to the surface of an infected cell will generally display peptide fragments from viral proteins, which can then be recognized by T_C lymphocytes. Mature viruses become vulnerable to the humoral immune system when they are released from the infected cell and are present for a time in the extracellular environment. Some are then ingested by macrophages (which ingest only those antigens that are recognized by the antibodies produced by a particular B cell). Viral peptide fragments will be displayed on the surfaces of the macrophages and B cells, complexed to class II MHC proteins, and the peptide antigens will trigger a multi-pronged response involving B cells, T_C cells, and T_H cells (Fig. 7–22).

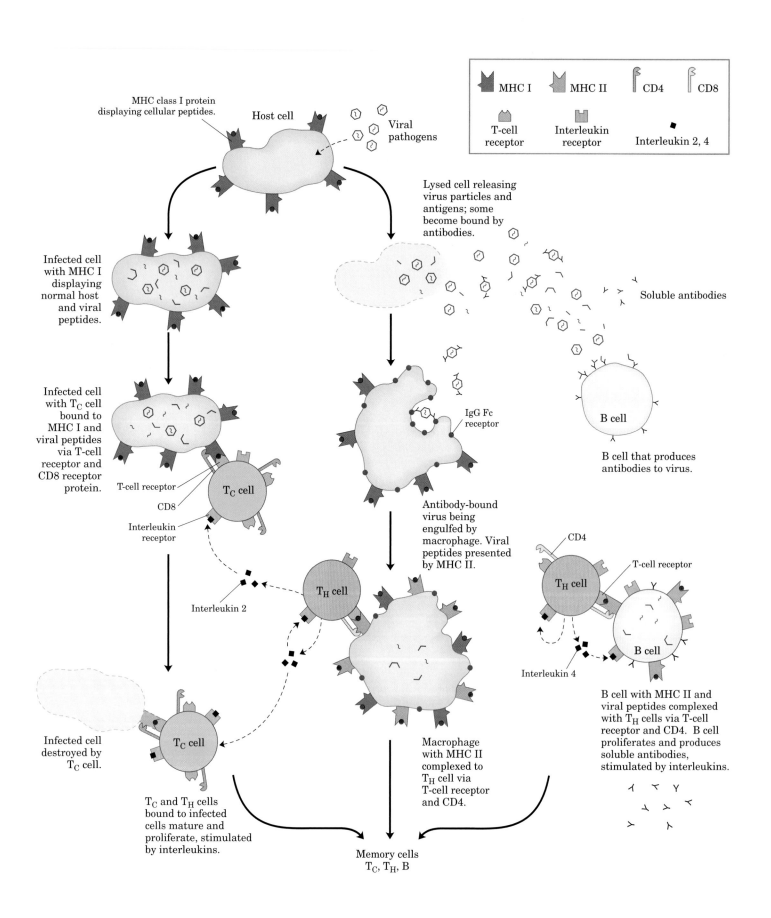

figure 7–22

Overview of the immune response to a viral infection. The individual steps are described in the text.

The class I MHC protein–peptide complexes on infected cells are recognized as foreign and bound by those T_C cells with T-cell receptors having the appropriate binding specificity. The T-cell receptors respond only to peptide antigens that are complexed to class I MHC proteins. The T_C cells have an additional receptor, **CD8,** also called a coreceptor, that enhances the binding interactions of T-cell receptors and MHC proteins (Fig. 7–22, middle left). The T_C cells live up to the name killer T cells by destroying the virally infected cell to which they are complexed through their T-cell receptors. Cell death is brought about by a number of mechanisms, not all well understood. One mechanism involves the release of a protein called **perforin,** which binds to and aggregates in the plasma membrane of the target cell, forming molecular pores that destroy the capacity of that cell to regulate its interior environment. T_C cells also induce a process called **programmed cell death,** or **apoptosis** (most commonly pronounced app′-a-toe′-sis), in which the cells complexed to T_C cells undergo metabolic changes that rapidly lead to the demise of the cell.

T_C cells with the proper specificity must proliferate selectively if large numbers of virus-infected cells are to be destroyed. To this end, T_C cells complexed to an infected cell generate cell-surface receptors for signaling proteins called **interleukins.** Interleukins, secreted by a variety of cells, stimulate the proliferation of only those T and B cells bearing the required interleukin receptors. Because T and B cells produce interleukin receptors only when they are complexed with an antigen, the only immune system cells that proliferate are those few that can respond to the antigen. The process of producing a population of cells by stimulated reproduction of a particular ancestor cell is called **clonal selection.**

The peptides complexed to class II MHC proteins and displayed on the surface of macrophages and B lymphocytes are similarly bound by the appropriate T-cell receptors of T_H cells. The T_H cells also have a coreceptor, called **CD4,** that enhances the binding interactions of the T-cell receptors. This overall binding interaction, in concert with secondary molecular signals that are currently being identified, activates the T_H cells. A subpopulation of activated T_H cells secrete a small signal protein called interleukin-2 (IL-2; M_r 15,000), which stimulates proliferation of nearby T_C cells and T_H cells having the appropriate interleukin receptors. This greatly increases the number of available immune system cells capable of recognizing and responding to the antigen. Another subpopulation of activated T_H cells complexed to macrophages or B lymphocytes secrete interleukin-4 (IL-4; M_r 20,000), which stimulates the proliferation of B cells that recognize the antigen (Fig. 7–22, bottom right). Proliferation of the responding B, T_C, and T_H cells continues as long as the appropriate antigen is present.

The proliferating B cells promote the destruction of any extracellular viruses or bacterial cells. They first secrete large amounts of soluble antibody that binds to the antigen. This bound antibody recruits a cellular system of about 20 proteins collectively called **complement** because they complement and enhance the action of the antibodies. The complement proteins disrupt the coats of many viruses or, in bacterial infections, produce holes in the cell walls of bacteria, causing them to swell and burst by osmotic shock.

Unlike T cells, B cells do not undergo selection in the thymus to eliminate those producing antibodies that recognize host (self) proteins. However, B cells do not contribute significantly to an immune response unless they are stimulated to proliferate by T_H cells. The T_H cells *do* undergo selection in the thymus, leaving no T_H cells capable of stimulating B cells that produce antibodies potentially dangerous to the host.

The T_H cells themselves participate only indirectly in the destruction of infected cells and pathogens, but their role is critical to the entire immune response. This is dramatically illustrated by the epidemic produced by HIV (human immunodeficiency virus), the virus that causes AIDS (acquired immune deficiency syndrome). The primary targets of HIV infection are T_H cells. Elimination of these cells progressively incapacitates the entire immune system.

Once antigen is depleted, activated immune cells generally die in a matter of days by programmed cell death. However, a few of the stimulated B and T cells mature into **memory cells.** These are long-lived cells that do not participate directly in the primary immune response when the antigen is first encountered. Instead they become permanent residents of the blood, ready to respond to a reappearance of the same antigen. Memory cells, when subsequently challenged by the antigen, can mount a secondary immune response that is generally much more rapid and vigorous than the primary response because of prior clonal expansion. By this mechanism, vertebrates once exposed to a virus or other pathogen can respond quickly to the pathogen when exposed again. This is the basis of the long-term immunity conferred by vaccines and the natural immunity to repeated infections by the same strain of a virus.

Antibodies Have Two Identical Antigen-Binding Sites

Immunoglobulin G (IgG) is the major class of antibody molecule and one of the most abundant proteins in the blood serum. IgG has four polypeptide chains: two large ones, called heavy chains, and two light chains, linked by noncovalent and disulfide bonds into a complex of M_r 150,000. The heavy chains of an IgG molecule interact at one end, then branch to interact separately with the light chains, forming a Y-shaped molecule (Fig. 7–23). At the "hinges" separating the base of an IgG molecule from its branches, the immunoglobulin can be cleaved with proteases. Cleavage with the protease papain liberates the basal fragment, called **Fc** because it usually *c*rystallizes readily, and the two branches, which are called **Fab,** the *a*ntigen-*b*inding fragments. Each branch has a single antigen-binding site.

figure 7–23
The structure of immunoglobulin G. (a) Pairs of heavy and light chains combine to form a Y-shaped molecule. Two antigen-binding sites are formed by the combination of variable domains from one light (V_L) and one heavy (V_H) chain. Cleavage with papain separates the Fab and Fc portions of the protein in the hinge region. The Fc portion of the molecule also contains bound carbohydrate. **(b)** A ribbon model of the first complete IgG molecule to be crystallized and structurally analyzed. Although the molecule contains two identical heavy chains (two shades of blue) and two identical light chains (two shades of red), it crystallized in the asymmetric conformation shown. Conformational flexibility may be important to the function of immunoglobulins.

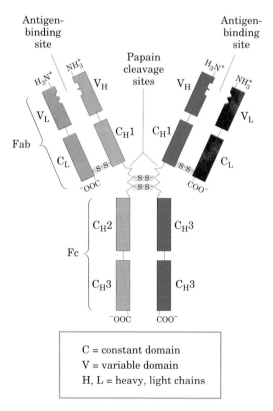

(a)

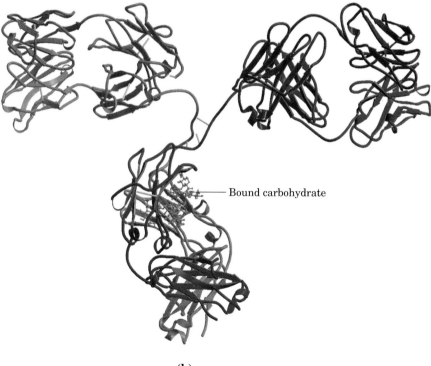

Bound carbohydrate

(b)

The fundamental structure of immunoglobulins was first established by Gerald Edelman and Rodney Porter. Each chain is made up of identifiable domains; some are constant in sequence and structure from one IgG to the next, others are variable. The constant domains have a characteristic structure known as the **immunoglobulin fold,** a well-conserved structural motif in the all-β class. There are three of these constant domains in each heavy chain and one in each light chain. The heavy and light chains also have one variable domain each, in which most of the variability in amino acid residue sequence is found. The variable domains associate to create the antigen-binding site (Fig. 7–24).

figure 7–24

Binding of IgG to an antigen. To generate an optimal fit for the antigen, the binding sites of IgG often undergo slight conformational changes. Such induced fit is common to many protein-ligand interactions.

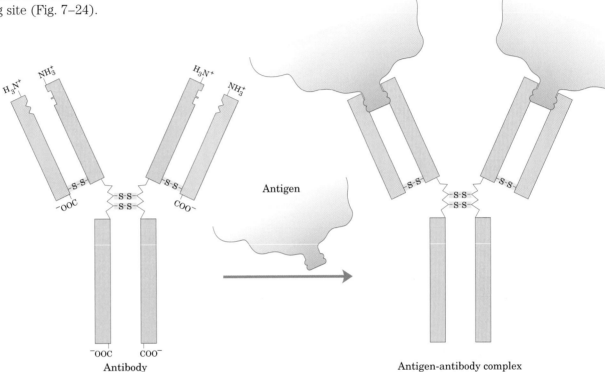

Antibody

Antigen

Antigen-antibody complex

In many vertebrates, IgG is only one of five classes of immunoglobulins. Each class has a characteristic type of heavy chain, denoted α, δ, ϵ, γ, and μ for IgA, IgD, IgE, IgG, and IgM, respectively. Two types of light chain, κ and λ, occur in all classes of immunoglobulins. The overall structures of **IgD** and **IgE** are similar to that of IgG. **IgM** occurs in either a monomeric, membrane-bound form or a secreted form that is a cross-linked pentamer of this basic structure (Fig. 7–25). **IgA,** found principally in secretions such as saliva, tears, and milk, can be a monomer, dimer, or trimer. IgM is the first antibody to be made by B lymphocytes and is the major antibody in the early stages of a primary immune response. Some B cells soon begin to produce IgD (with the same antigen-binding site as the IgM produced by the same cell), but the unique function of IgD is less clear.

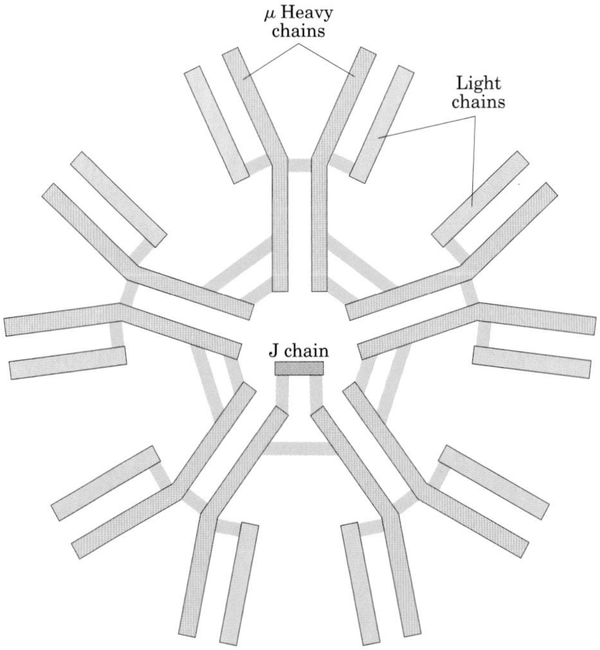

μ Heavy chains

Light chains

J chain

figure 7–25

IgM pentamer of immunoglobulin units. The pentamer is cross-linked with disulfide bonds. The J chain is a polypeptide of M_r 20,000 found in both IgA and IgM.

The IgG described above is the major antibody in secondary immune responses, which are initiated by memory B cells. As part of the organism's ongoing immunity to antigens already encountered and dealt with, IgG is the most abundant immunoglobulin in the blood. When IgG binds to an invading bacterium or virus, it not only activates the complement system, but also activates certain leukocytes such as macrophages to engulf and destroy the invader. Yet another class of receptors on the cell surface of macrophages recognizes and binds the Fc region of IgG. When these Fc receptors bind an antibody-pathogen complex, the macrophage engulfs the complex by phagocytosis (Fig. 7–26).

figure 7–26

Phagocytosis of an antibody-bound virus by a macrophage. The Fc regions of the antibodies bind to Fc receptors on the surface of the macrophage, triggering the macrophage to engulf and destroy the virus.

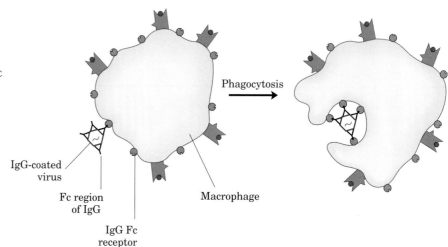

IgG-coated virus

Fc region of IgG

IgG Fc receptor

Phagocytosis

Macrophage

IgE plays an important role in the allergic response, interacting with basophils (phagocytic leukocytes) in the blood and histamine-secreting cells called mast cells that are widely distributed in tissues. This immunoglobulin binds, through its Fc region, to special Fc receptors on the basophils or mast cells. In this form, IgE serves as a kind of receptor for antigen. If antigen is bound, the cells are induced to secrete histamine and other biologically active amines that cause dilation and increased permeability of blood vessels. These effects on the blood vessels are thought to facilitate the movement of immune system cells and proteins to sites of inflammation. They also produce the symptoms normally associated with allergies. Pollen or other allergens are recognized as foreign, triggering an immune response normally reserved for pathogens.

Antibodies Bind Tightly and Specifically to Antigen

The binding specificity of an antibody is determined by the amino acid residues in the variable domains of its heavy and light chains. Many residues in these domains are variable, but not equally so. Some, particularly those lining the antigen-binding site, are hypervariable—especially likely to differ. Specificity is conferred by chemical complementarity between the antigen and its specific binding site, in terms of shape and the location of charged, nonpolar, and hydrogen-bonding groups. For example, a binding site with a negatively charged group may bind an antigen with a positive charge in the complementary position. In many instances, complementarity is achieved interactively as the structures of antigen and binding site are influenced by each other during the approach of the ligand. Conformational changes in the antibody and/or the antigen then occur that allow the complementary groups to interact fully. This is an example of induced fit (Fig. 7–27).

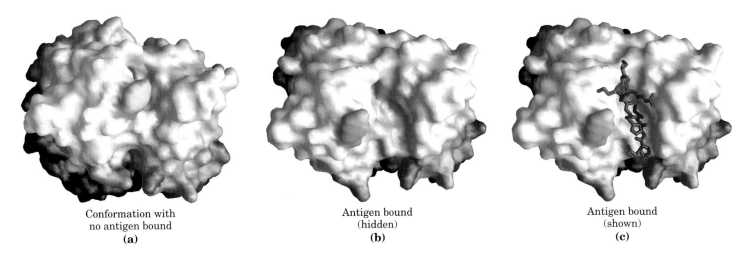

Conformation with
no antigen bound
(a)

Antigen bound
(hidden)
(b)

Antigen bound
(shown)
(c)

figure 7–27

Induced fit in the binding of an antigen to IgG. The molecule, shown in surface contour, is the Fab fragment of an IgG. The antigen this IgG binds is a small peptide derived from HIV. Two residues from the heavy chain (blue) and one from the light chain (pink) are colored to provide visual points of reference. **(a)** View of the Fab fragment looking down on the antigen-binding site. **(b)** The same view, but here the Fab fragment is in the "bound" conformation; the antigen has been omitted from the image to provide an unobstructed view of the altered binding site. Note how the binding cavity has enlarged and several groups have shifted position. **(c)** The same view as in **(b),** but with the antigen pictured in the binding site as a red stick structure.

A typical antibody-antigen interaction is quite strong, characterized by K_d values as low as 10^{-10} M (recall that a lower K_d corresponds to a stronger binding interaction). The K_d reflects the energy derived from the various ionic, hydrogen-bonding, hydrophobic, and van der Waals interactions that stabilize the binding. The binding energy required to produce a K_d of 10^{-10} M is about 65 kJ/mol.

A complex of a peptide derived from HIV (a model antigen) and an Fab molecule illustrates some of these properties (Fig. 7–27). The changes in structure observed on antigen binding are particularly striking in this example.

The Antibody-Antigen Interaction Is the Basis for a Variety of Important Analytical Procedures

The extraordinary binding affinity and specificity of antibodies makes them valuable analytical reagents. Two types of antibody preparations are in use: polyclonal and monoclonal. **Polyclonal antibodies** are those produced by many different B lymphocytes responding to one antigen, such as a protein injected into an animal. Cells in the population of B lymphocytes produce antibodies that bind specific, different epitopes within the antigen. Thus, polyclonal preparations contain a mixture of antibodies that recognize different parts of the protein. **Monoclonal antibodies,** in contrast, are synthesized by a population of identical B cells (a **clone**) grown in cell culture. These antibodies are homogeneous, all recognizing the same epitope. The techniques for producing monoclonal antibodies were developed by Georges Köhler and Cesar Milstein.

The specificity of antibodies has practical uses. A selected antibody can be covalently attached to a resin and used in a chromatography column of the type shown in Figure 5–18c. When a mixture of proteins is added to the column, the antibody will specifically bind its target protein and retain it on the column while other proteins are washed through. The target protein can then be eluted from the resin by a salt solution or some other agent. This is a powerful tool for protein purification.

In another versatile analytical technique, an antibody is attached to a radioactive label or some other reagent that makes it easy to detect. When the antibody binds the target protein, the label reveals the presence of the protein in a solution or its location in a gel or even a living cell. Several variations of this procedure are illustrated in Figure 7–28.

Georges Köhler

Cesar Milstein

figure 7–28

Antibody techniques. The specific reaction of an antibody with its antigen is the basis of several techniques that identify and quantify a specific protein in a complex sample. **(a)** A schematic representation of the general method. **(b)** An ELISA testing for the presence of herpes simplex virus (HSV) antibodies in blood samples. Wells were coated with an HSV antigen, to which antibodies against HSV in a patient's blood will bind. The second antibody is anti–human IgG linked to horseradish peroxidase. Blood samples with greater amounts of HSV antibody turn brighter yellow. **(c)** An immunoblot. Lanes 1 to 3 are from an SDS gel; samples from successive stages in the purification of a protein kinase have been separated and stained with Coomassie blue. Lanes 4 to 6 show the same samples, but these were electrophoretically transferred to a nitrocellulose membrane after separation on an SDS gel. The membrane was then "probed" with antibody against the protein kinase. The numbers between the gel and the immunoblot indicate M_r ($\times 10^{-3}$).

An **ELISA** (enzyme-linked immunosorbent assay) allows for rapid screening and quantification of the presence of an antigen in a sample (Fig. 7–28b). Proteins in a sample are adsorbed to an inert surface, usually a 96-well polystyrene plate. The surface is washed with a solution of an inexpensive nonspecific protein (often casein from nonfat dry milk powder) to block proteins in subsequent steps from also adsorbing to these surfaces. The surface is then treated with a solution containing the primary antibody—an antibody against the protein of interest. Unbound antibody is washed away and the surface is treated with a solution containing antibodies against the primary antibody. These secondary antibodies have been linked to an enzyme that catalyzes a reaction that forms a colored product. After unbound secondary antibody is washed away, the substrate of the antibody-linked enzyme is added. Product formation (monitored as color intensity) is proportional to the concentration of the protein of interest in the sample.

In an **immunoblot assay** (Fig. 7–28c), proteins that have been separated by gel electrophoresis are transferred electrophoretically to a nitrocellulose membrane. The membrane is blocked (as described above for ELISA), then treated successively with primary antibody, secondary antibody linked to enzyme, and substrate. A colored precipitate forms only along the band containing the protein of interest. The immunoblot allows

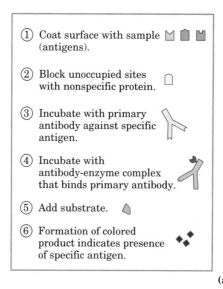

① Coat surface with sample (antigens).

② Block unoccupied sites with nonspecific protein.

③ Incubate with primary antibody against specific antigen.

④ Incubate with antibody-enzyme complex that binds primary antibody.

⑤ Add substrate.

⑥ Formation of colored product indicates presence of specific antigen.

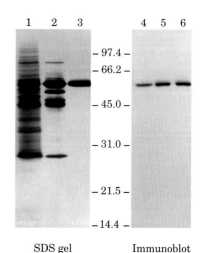

(a)

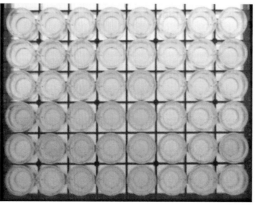

ELISA assay

(b)

— 97.4 —
— 66.2 —
— 45.0 —
— 31.0 —
— 21.5 —
— 14.4 —

SDS gel   Immunoblot

(c)

the detection of a minor component in a sample and provides an approximation of its molecular weight.

We will encounter other aspects of antibodies in later chapters. They are extremely important in medicine and can tell us much about the structure of proteins and the action of genes.

Protein Interactions Modulated by Chemical Energy: Actin, Myosin, and Molecular Motors

Organisms move. Cells move. Organelles and macromolecules within cells move. Most of these movements arise from the activity of the fascinating class of protein-based molecular motors. Fueled by chemical energy, usually derived from ATP, large aggregates of motor proteins undergo cyclic conformational changes that accumulate into a unified, directional force—the tiny force that pulls apart chromosomes in a dividing cell, and the immense force that levers a pouncing, quarter-ton jungle cat into the air.

The interactions among motor proteins, as you might predict, feature complementary arrangements of ionic, hydrogen-bonding, hydrophobic, and van der Waals interactions at protein binding sites. In motor proteins, however, these interactions achieve exceptionally high levels of spatial and temporal organization.

Motor proteins underlie the contraction of muscles, the migration of organelles along microtubules, the rotation of bacterial flagella, and the movement of some proteins along DNA. As we noted in Chapter 2, proteins called kinesins and dyneins move along microtubules in cells, pulling along organelles or reorganizing chromosomes during cell division. An interaction of dynein with microtubules brings about the motion of eukaryotic flagella and cilia. Flagellar motion in bacteria involves a complex rotational motor at the base of the flagellum. Helicases, polymerases, and other proteins move along DNA as they carry out their functions in DNA metabolism. Here, we focus on the well-studied example of the contractile proteins of vertebrate skeletal muscle as a paradigm for how proteins translate chemical energy into motion.

The Major Proteins of Muscle Are Myosin and Actin

The contractile force of muscle is generated by the interaction of two proteins, myosin and actin. These proteins are arranged in filaments that undergo transient interactions and slide past each other to bring about contraction. Together, actin and myosin make up over 80% of the protein mass of muscle.

Myosin (M_r 540,000) has six subunits: two heavy chains (M_r 220,000) and four light chains (M_r 20,000). The heavy chains account for much of the overall structure. At their carboxyl termini, they are arranged as extended α helices, wrapped around each other in a fibrous, left-handed coiled coil similar to that of α-keratin (Fig. 7–29a). At its amino termini, each heavy chain has a large globular domain containing a site where ATP is hydrolyzed. The light chains are associated with the globular domains.

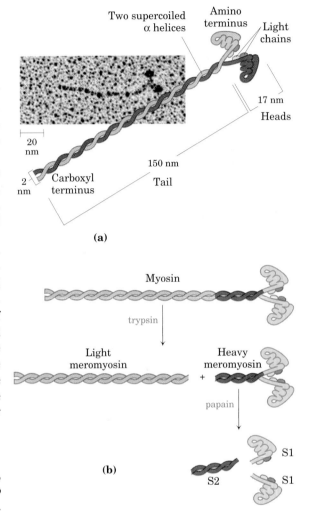

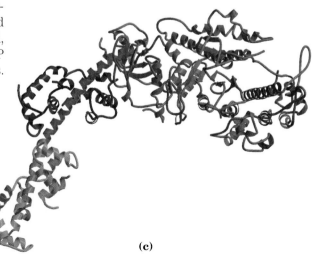

figure 7–29
Myosin. (a) Myosin has two heavy chains (in two shades of pink), the carboxyl termini forming an extended coiled coil (tail) and the amino termini having globular domains (heads). Two light chains (blue) are associated with each myosin head. **(b)** Cleavage with trypsin and papain separates the myosin heads (S1 fragments) from the tails. **(c)** Ribbon representation of the myosin S1 fragment. The heavy chain is in gray, the two light chains in two shades of blue.

When myosin is treated briefly with the protease trypsin, much of the fibrous tail is cleaved off, dividing the protein into components called light and heavy meromyosin (Fig. 7–29b). The globular domain, called myosin subfragment 1, or S1, or simply the myosin head group, is liberated from heavy meromyosin by cleavage with papain. The S1 fragment produced by this procedure is the motor domain that makes muscle contraction possible. S1 fragments can be crystallized, and their structure has been determined. The overall structure of the S1 fragment as determined by Ivan Rayment and Hazel Holden is shown in Figure 7–29c.

In muscle cells, molecules of myosin aggregate to form structures called **thick filaments** (Fig. 7–30a). These rodlike structures serve as the core of the contractile unit. Within a thick filament, several hundred myosin molecules are arranged with their fibrous "tails" associated to form a long bipolar structure. The globular domains project from either end of this structure, in regular stacked arrays.

The second major muscle protein, **actin,** is abundant in almost all eukaryotic cells. In muscle, molecules of monomeric actin, called G-actin (*g*lobular actin; M_r 42,000), associate to form a long polymer called F-actin (*f*ilamentous actin). The **thin filament** (Fig. 7–30b) consists of F-actin, along with the proteins troponin and tropomyosin. The filamentous parts of thin filaments assemble as successive monomeric actin molecules add to one end. On addition, each monomer binds ATP, then hydrolyzes it to ADP, so all actin molecules in the filament are complexed to ADP. However, this ATP hydrolysis by actin functions only in the assembly of the filaments; it does not contribute directly to the energy expended in muscle contraction. Each actin monomer in the thin filament can bind tightly and specifically to one myosin head group (Fig. 7–30c).

figure 7–30
The major components of muscle. (a) Myosin aggregates to form a bipolar structure called a thick filament. **(b)** F-actin is a filamentous assemblage of G-actin monomers that polymerize two by two, giving the appearance of two filaments spiraling about one another in a right-handed fashion. An electron micrograph and a model of F-actin are shown. **(c)** Space-filling model of an actin filament (red) with one myosin head (gray and two shades of blue) bound to an actin monomer within the filament.

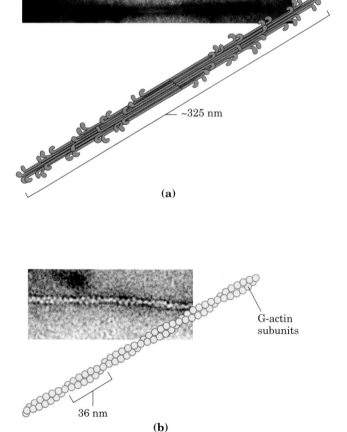

~325 nm

(a)

36 nm

G-actin subunits

(b)

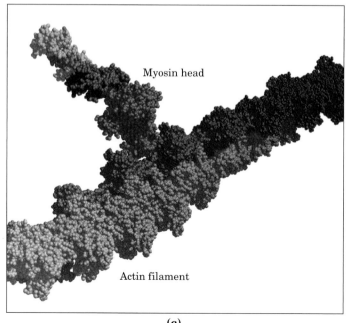

Myosin head

Actin filament

(c)

Additional Proteins Organize the Thin and Thick Filaments into Ordered Structures

Skeletal muscle consists of parallel bundles of **muscle fibers,** each fiber a single, very large, multinucleated cell, 20 to 100 μm in diameter, formed from many cells fused together and often spanning the length of the muscle. Each fiber, in turn, contains about 1,000 **myofibrils,** 2 μm in diameter, each consisting of a vast number of regularly arrayed thick and thin filaments complexed to other proteins (Fig. 7–31). A system of flat membranous vesicles called the **sarcoplasmic reticulum** surrounds each myofibril. Examined under the electron microscope, muscle fibers reveal alternating regions of high and low electron density, called the **A** and **I bands** (Fig. 7–31b,c). The A and I bands arise from the arrangement of

figure 7–31
Structure of skeletal muscle. (a) Muscle fibers consist of single, elongated, multinucleated cells that arise from the fusion of many precursor cells. Within the fibers are many myofibrils surrounded by the membranous sarcoplasmic reticulum. The organization of thick and thin filaments in the myofibril gives it a striated appearance. When muscle contracts, the I bands narrow and the Z disks come closer together, as seen in electron micrographs of relaxed **(b)** and contracted **(c)** muscle.

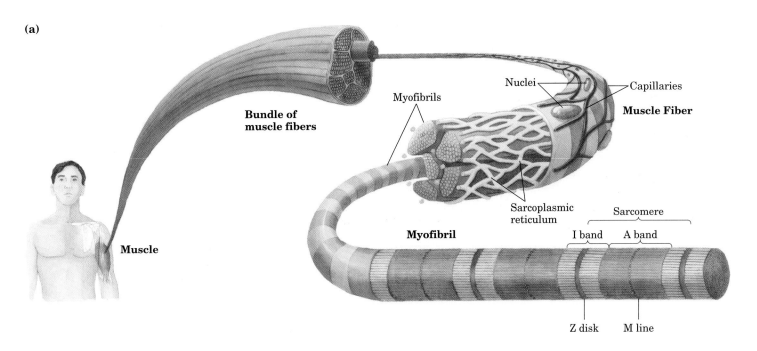

(a)

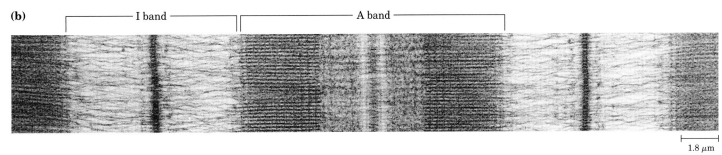

(b)

(c)

thick and thin filaments, which are aligned and partially overlapping. The I band is the region of the bundle that in cross section would contain only thin filaments. The darker A band stretches the length of the thick filament and includes the region where parallel thick and thin filaments overlap. Bisecting the I band is a thin structure called the **Z disk,** perpendicular to the thin filaments and serving as an anchor to which the thin filaments are attached. The A band too is bisected by a thin line, the **M line** or M disk, a region of high electron density in the middle of the thick filaments. The entire contractile unit, consisting of bundles of thick filaments interleaved at either end with bundles of thin filaments, is called the **sarcomere.** The arrangement of interleaved bundles allows the thick and thin filaments to slide past each other (by a mechanism discussed below), causing a progressive shortening of each sarcomere (Fig. 7–32).

The thin actin filaments are attached at one end to the Z disk in a regular pattern. The assembly includes the minor muscle proteins **α-actinin, desmin,** and **vimentin.** Thin filaments also contain a large protein called **nebulin** (~7,000 amino acid residues), thought to be structured as an α helix long enough to span the length of the filament. The M line similarly

figure 7–32
Muscle contraction. Thick filaments are bipolar structures created by the association of many myosin molecules. **(a)** Muscle contraction occurs by the sliding of the thick and thin filaments past each other so that the Z disks in neighboring I bands approach each other. **(b)** The thick and thin filaments are interleaved such that each thick filament is surrounded by six thin filaments.

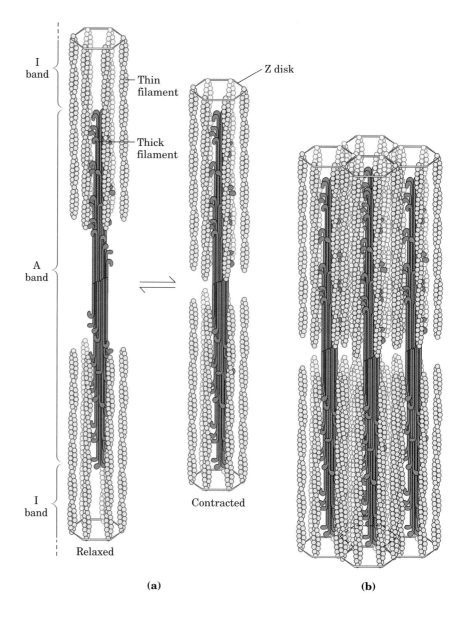

I
band

Thin
filament

Z disk

Thick
filament

A
band

Contracted

I
band

Relaxed

(a)

(b)

organizes the thick filaments. It contains the proteins **paramyosin, C-protein,** and **M-protein.** Another class of proteins called **titins,** the largest known single polypeptide chains (the titin of human cardiac muscle has 26,926 amino acid residues), link the thick filaments to the Z disk, providing additional organization to the overall structure. Among their structural functions, the proteins nebulin and titin are believed to act as "molecular rulers," regulating the length of the thin and thick filaments, respectively. Titin extends from the Z disk to the M line, regulating the length of the sarcomere itself and preventing overextension of the muscle. The characteristic sarcomere length varies from one muscle tissue to the next in a vertebrate organism, attributed in large part to the expression of different titin variants.

Myosin Thick Filaments Slide along Actin Thin Filaments

The interaction between actin and myosin, like that between all proteins and ligands, involves weak bonds. When ATP is not bound to myosin, a face on the myosin head group binds tightly to actin (Fig. 7–33). When ATP binds to myosin and is hydrolyzed to ADP and phosphate, a coordinated and cyclic series of conformational changes occur in which myosin releases the F-actin subunit and binds another subunit farther along the thin filament.

The cycle has four major steps (Fig. 7–33). ① ATP binds to myosin, and a cleft in the myosin molecule opens, disrupting the actin-myosin interaction so that the bound actin is released. ATP is then hydrolyzed (step ②), causing a conformational change in the protein to a "high-energy" state that moves the myosin head and changes its orientation in relation to the actin thin filament. Myosin then binds weakly to an F-actin subunit closer to the Z disk than the one just released. As the phosphate product of ATP hydrolysis is released from myosin in step ③, another conformational change occurs in which the myosin cleft closes, strengthening the myosin-actin binding. This is followed quickly by the final step, ④, a "power stroke" during which the conformation of the myosin head returns to the original resting state, its orientation relative to the bound actin changing so as to pull the tail of the myosin toward the Z disk. ADP is then released to complete the cycle. Each cycle generates about 3 to 4 pN (piconewtons) of force and moves the thick filament 5 to 10 nm relative to the thin filament.

Because there are many myosin heads in a thick filament, at any given moment some (probably 1% to 3%) are bound to the thin filaments. This prevents the thick filaments from slipping backward when an individual myosin head releases the actin subunit to which it was bound. The thick filament thus actively slides forward past the adjacent thin filaments. This process, coordinated among the many sarcomeres in a muscle fiber, brings about muscle contraction.

The interaction between actin and myosin must be regulated so that contraction occurs only in response to appropriate signals from the nervous

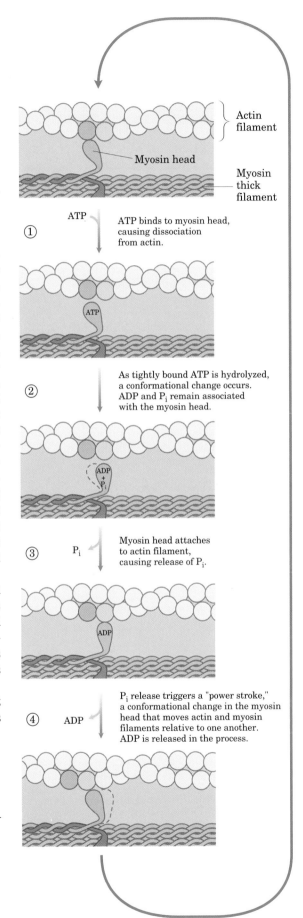

Actin filament

Myosin head

Myosin thick filament

① ATP — ATP binds to myosin head, causing dissociation from actin.

② — As tightly bound ATP is hydrolyzed, a conformational change occurs. ADP and P_i remain associated with the myosin head.

③ P_i — Myosin head attaches to actin filament, causing release of P_i.

④ ADP — P_i release triggers a "power stroke," a conformational change in the myosin head that moves actin and myosin filaments relative to one another. ADP is released in the process.

figure 7–33
Molecular mechanism of muscle contraction. Conformational changes in the myosin head that are coupled to stages in the ATP hydrolytic cycle cause myosin to successively dissociate from one actin subunit, then associate with another farther along the actin filament. In this way the myosin heads slide along the thin filaments, drawing the thick filament array into the thin filament array (see Fig. 7–32).

system. The regulation is mediated by a complex of two proteins, **tropomyosin** and **troponin.** Tropomyosin binds to the thin filament, blocking the attachment sites for the myosin head groups. Troponin is a Ca^{2+}-binding protein. A nerve impulse causes release of Ca^{2+} from the sarcoplasmic reticulum. The released Ca^{2+} binds to troponin (another protein-ligand interaction) and causes a conformational change in the tropomyosin-troponin complexes, exposing the myosin-binding sites on the thin filaments. Contraction follows.

Working skeletal muscle requires two types of molecular functions that are common in proteins—binding and catalysis. The actin-myosin interaction, a protein-ligand interaction like that of immunoglobulins with antigens, is reversible and leaves the participants unchanged. When ATP binds myosin, however, it is hydrolyzed to ADP and P_i. Myosin is not only an actin-binding protein, it is also an ATPase—an enzyme. The function of enzymes in catalyzing chemical transformations is the topic of the next chapter.

summary

Protein function often entails interactions with other molecules. A molecule bound by a protein is called a ligand, and the site on the protein to which it binds is called the binding site. Proteins are not rigid and may undergo conformational changes when a ligand binds, a process called induced fit. In a multisubunit protein, the binding of a ligand to one subunit may affect ligand binding to other subunits. Ligand binding can be regulated. Oxygen-binding proteins, immune system proteins, and motor proteins are useful models with which to illustrate these principles.

Myoglobin and hemoglobin contain a prosthetic group called heme to which oxygen binds. Heme consists of a single atom of Fe^{2+} iron coordinated within a porphyrin. Some other small molecules, such as CO and NO, can also bind heme. Myoglobin is a single polypeptide with eight α-helical regions connected by bends. It has a single molecule of heme, located in a pocket deep within the polypeptide. Oxygen binds to myoglobin reversibly. Simple reversible binding can be described by an association constant K_a or a dissociation constant K_d. For a monomeric protein, the fraction of binding sites occupied by a ligand is a hyperbolic function of ligand concentration. Because O_2 is a gas, the term P_{50}, which describes the partial pressure of oxygen at which an O_2-binding protein is half saturated with bound oxygen, is used in place of K_d. The entry and exit of O_2 depend upon small molecular motions, called "breathing," of the myoglobin molecule.

Normal adult hemoglobin has four heme-containing subunits, two α and two β. They are similar in structure to each other and to myoglobin. Strong interactions occur between unlike (α and β) subunits. Hemoglobin exists in two interchangeable states, called T and R. The T state is stabilized by several salt bridges and is most stable when oxygen is not bound. Oxygen binding promotes a transition to the R state.

Oxygen binding to hemoglobin is both allosteric and cooperative. Binding of O_2 to one binding site of hemoglobin affects binding of O_2 to other such sites, an example of allosteric binding behavior. Conformational changes between the T and R states, mediated by subunit-subunit interactions, give rise to a form of allostery called cooperative binding. Cooperative binding results in a sigmoid binding curve and can be analyzed by a Hill plot. Two major models have been proposed to explain the cooperative binding of ligands to multisubunit proteins. In the concerted model, all subunits are in the same conformation at any given time, and the entire protein undergoes a reversible transition between two possible conformations. Successive binding of ligand molecules to the low-affinity conformation facilitates transition to the high-affinity conformation. In the sequential model, individual subunits can undergo conformational changes. Binding of a ligand to one subunit alters that subunit's conformation, facilitating similar changes in, and binding of additional ligands to, the other subunits.

Hemoglobin also binds H^+ and CO_2. In both cases, binding results in the formation of ion pairs that stabilize the T state and O_2 binding is weakened, a phenomenon called the Bohr effect. The binding of H^+ and CO_2 to hemoglobin in the tissues promotes the release of O_2, and the binding of O_2 to hemoglobin in the lungs promotes the release of H^+ and CO_2. Oxygen binding to hemoglobin is also modulated by 2,3-bisphosphoglycerate, which binds to and stabilizes the T state.

Sickle-cell anemia is a genetic disease caused by a single amino acid substitution (Glu to Val) at position 6 in the β chains of hemoglobin. The change produces a hydrophobic patch on the surface of the protein that causes the hemoglobin molecules to aggregate into bundles of fibers. These bundles give the erythrocytes a sickle shape. This homozygous condition results in serious medical complications.

The immune response is mediated by interactions among an array of specialized leukocytes and their associated proteins. T lymphocytes produce T-cell receptors. B lymphocytes produce immunoglobulins. All cells produce MHC proteins, which display host (self) or antigenic (nonself) peptides on the cell surface. Helper T cells induce the proliferation of those B cells and cytotoxic T cells producing immunoglobulins or T-cell receptors that bind to a specific antigen, a process called clonal selection.

Humans have five classes of immunoglobulins, each with different biological functions. The most abundant is IgG, a Y-shaped protein with two heavy and two light chains. The domains near the upper ends of the Y are hypervariable within the broad population of IgGs and form two antigen-binding sites. A given immunoglobulin generally binds to only a part, called the epitope, of a large antigen. Binding often involves a conformational change in the IgG, an induced fit to the antigen.

Protein-ligand interactions achieve a special degree of spatial and temporal organization in motor proteins. Muscle contraction results from choreographed interactions between myosin and actin, coupled to the hydrolysis of ATP by myosin. Myosin consists of two heavy and four light chains, forming a fibrous coiled coil (tail) domain and a globular (head) domain. Myosin molecules are organized into thick filaments, which slide past thin filaments composed largely of actin. ATP hydrolysis in myosin is coupled to a series of conformational changes in the myosin head, leading to dissociation of myosin from one F-actin subunit and its eventual reassociation with another F-actin subunit farther along the thin filament. The myosin thus slides along the actin filaments. Muscle contraction is stimulated by the release of Ca^{2+} from the sarcoplasmic reticulum. The Ca^{2+} binds to the protein troponin, leading to a conformational change in a troponin-tropomyosin complex that triggers the cycle of actin-myosin interactions.

further reading

Oxygen-Binding Proteins

Ackers, G.K. & Hazzard, J.H. (1993) Transduction of binding energy into hemoglobin cooperativity. *Trends Biochem. Sci.* **18**, 385–390.

Changeux, J.-P. (1993) Allosteric proteins: from regulatory enzymes to receptors—personal recollections. *Bioessays* **15**, 625–634.

An interesting perspective from a leader in the field.

Dickerson, R.E. & Geis, I. (1982) *Hemoglobin: Structure, Function, Evolution, and Pathology,* The Benjamin/Cummings Publishing Company, Redwood City, CA.

di Prisco, G., Condò, S.G., Tamburrini, M., & Giardina, B. (1991) Oxygen transport in extreme environments. *Trends Biochem. Sci.* **16**, 471–474.

A revealing comparison of the oxygen-binding properties of hemoglobins from polar species.

Koshland, D.E., Jr., Nemethy, G., & Filmer, D. (1966) Comparison of experimental binding data and theoretical models in proteins containing subunits. *Biochemistry* **6**, 365–385.

The paper in which the sequential model is introduced.

Monod, J., Wyman, J., & Changeux, J.-P. (1965) On the nature of allosteric transitions: a plausible model. *J. Mol. Biol.* **12**, 88–118.

The concerted model was first proposed in this landmark paper.

Olson, J.S. & Phillips, G.N., Jr. (1996) Kinetic pathways and barriers for ligand binding to myoglobin. *J. Biol. Chem.* **271**, 17,593–17,596.

Perutz, M.F. (1989) Myoglobin and haemoglobin: role of distal residues in reactions with haem ligands. *Trends Biochem. Sci.* **14**, 42–44.

Perutz, M.F., Wilkinson, A.J., Paoli, M., & Dodson, G.G. (1998) The stereochemical mechanism of the cooperative effects in hemoglobin revisited. *Annu. Rev. Biophys. Biomol. Struct.* **27,** 1–34.

Immune System Proteins

Blom, B., Res, P.C., & Spits, H. (1998) T cell precursors in man and mice. *Crit. Rev. Immunol.* **18,** 371–388.

Cohen, I.R. (1988) The self, the world and autoimmunity. *Sci. Am.* **258** (April), 52–60.

Davies, D.R. & Chacko, S. (1993) Antibody structure. *Acc. Chem. Res.* **26,** 421–427.

Davies, D.R., Padlan, E.A., & Sheriff, S. (1990) Antibody-antigen complexes. *Annu. Rev. Biochem.* **59,** 439–473.

Davis, M.M. (1990) T cell receptor gene diversity and selection. *Annu. Rev. Biochem.* **59,** 475–496.

Dutton, R.W., Bradley, L.M., & Swain, S.L. (1998) T cell memory. *Annu. Rev. Immunol.* **16,** 201–223.

Life, Death and the Immune System. (1993) *Sci. Am.* **269** (September).

A special issue on the immune system.

Marrack, P. & Kappler, J. (1987) The T cell receptor. *Science* **238,** 1073–1079.

Müller-Eberhard, H.J. (1988) Molecular organization and function of the complement system. *Annu. Rev. Biochem.* **57,** 321–337.

Parham, P. & Ohta, T. (1996) Population biology of antigen presentation by MHC class I molecules. *Science* **272,** 67–74.

Ploegh, H.L. (1998) Viral strategies of immune evasion. *Science* **280,** 248–253.

Thomsen, A.R., Nansen, A., & Christensen, J.P. (1998) Virus-induced T cell activation and the inflammatory response. *Curr. Top. Microbiol. Immunol.* **231,** 99–123.

Van Parjis, L. & Abbas, A.K. (1998) Homeostasis and self-tolerance in the immune system: turning lymphocytes off. *Science* **280,** 243–248.

York, I.A. & Rock, K.L. (1996) Antigen processing and presentation by the class-I major histocompatibility complex. *Annu. Rev. Immunol.* **14,** 369–396.

Molecular Motors

Finer, J.T., Simmons, R.M., & Spudich, J.A. (1994) Single myosin molecule mechanics: piconewton forces and nanometre steps. *Nature* **368,** 113–119.

Modern techniques reveal the forces affecting individual motor proteins.

Goldman, Y.E. (1998) Wag the tail: structural dynamics of actomyosin. *Cell* **93,** 1–4.

Huxley, H.E. (1998) Getting to grips with contraction: the interplay of structure and biochemistry. *Trends Biochem. Sci.* **23,** 84–87.

An interesting historical perspective on deciphering the mechanism of muscle contraction.

Labeit, S. & Kolmerer, B. (1995) Titins: giant proteins in charge of muscle ultrastructure and elasticity. *Science* **270,** 293–296.

A structural and functional description of some of the largest known proteins.

Rayment, I. (1996) The structural basis of the myosin ATPase activity. *J. Biol. Chem.* **271,** 15,850–15,853.

Examining mechanism from a structural perspective.

Rayment, I. & Holden, H.M. (1994) The three-dimensional structure of a molecular motor. *Trends Biochem. Sci.* **19,** 129–134.

Spudich, J.A. (1994) How molecular motors work. *Nature* **372,** 515–518.

problems

1. Relationship between Affinity and Dissociation Constant Protein A has a binding site for ligand X with a K_d of 10^{-6} M. Protein B has a binding site for ligand X with a K_d of 10^{-9} M. Which protein has a higher affinity for ligand X? Explain your reasoning. Convert the K_d to K_a for both proteins.

2. Negative Cooperativity Which of the following situations would produce a Hill plot with $n_H < 1.0$? Explain your reasoning in each case.

(a) The protein has multiple subunits, each with a single ligand-binding site. Binding of ligand to one site decreases the binding affinity of other sites for the ligand.

(b) The protein is a single polypeptide with two ligand-binding sites, each having a different affinity for the ligand.

(c) The protein is a single polypeptide with a single ligand-binding site. As purified, the protein preparation is heterogeneous, containing some protein molecules that are partially denatured and thus have a lower binding affinity for the ligand.

3. Affinity for Oxygen in Myoglobin and Hemoglobin What is the effect of the following changes on the O_2 affinity of myoglobin and hemoglobin? (a) A drop in the pH of blood plasma from 7.4 to 7.2. (b) A decrease in the partial pressure of CO_2 in the lungs from 6 kPa (holding one's breath) to 2 kPa (normal). (c) An increase in the BPG level from 5 mM (normal altitudes) to 8 mM (high altitudes).

4. Cooperativity in Hemoglobin Under appropriate conditions, hemoglobin dissociates into its four subunits. The isolated α subunit binds oxygen, but the O_2-saturation curve is hyperbolic rather than sigmoid. In addition, the binding of oxygen to the isolated α subunit is not affected by the presence of H^+, CO_2, or BPG. What do these observations indicate about the source of the cooperativity in hemoglobin?

5. Comparison of Fetal and Maternal Hemoglobins Studies of oxygen transport in pregnant mammals have shown that the O_2-saturation curves of fetal and maternal blood are markedly different when measured under the same conditions. Fetal erythrocytes contain a structural variant of hemoglobin, HbF, consisting of two α and two γ subunits ($\alpha_2\gamma_2$), whereas maternal erythrocytes contain HbA ($\alpha_2\beta_2$).

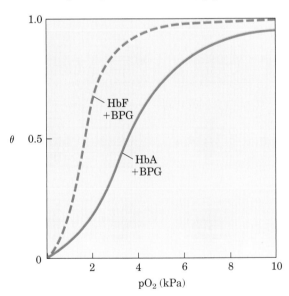

(a) Which hemoglobin has a higher affinity for oxygen under physiological conditions, HbA or HbF? Explain.

(b) What is the physiological significance of the different O_2 affinities?

(c) When all the BPG is carefully removed from samples of HbA and HbF, the measured O_2-saturation curves (and consequently the O_2 affinities) are displaced to the left. However, HbA now has a greater affinity for oxygen than does HbF. When BPG is reintroduced, the O_2-saturation curves return to normal, as shown in the graph. What is the effect of BPG on the O_2 affinity of hemoglobin? How can the above information be used to explain the different O_2 affinities of fetal and maternal hemoglobin?

6. Hemoglobin Variants There are almost 500 naturally occurring variants of hemoglobin. Most are the result of a single amino acid substitution in a globin polypeptide chain. Some variants produce clinical illness, though not all variants have deleterious effects. A brief sample is presented below:

HbS (sickle-cell Hb): substitutes a Val for a Glu on the surface

Hb Cowtown: eliminates an ion pair involved in T-state stabilization

Hb Memphis: substitutes one uncharged polar residue for another of similar size on the surface

Hb Bibba: substitutes a Pro for a Leu involved in an α helix

Hb Milwaukee: substitutes a Glu for a Val

Hb Providence: substitutes an Asn for a Lys that normally projects into the central cavity of the tetramer

Hb Philly: substitutes a Phe for a Tyr, disrupting hydrogen bonding at the $\alpha_1\beta_1$ interface

Explain your choices for each of the following:

(a) The Hb variant *least* likely to cause pathological symptoms.

(b) The variant(s) most likely to show pI values different from that of HbA when run on an isoelectric focusing gel.

(c) The variant(s) most likely to show a decrease in BPG binding and an increase in the overall affinity of the hemoglobin for oxygen.

7. Reversible (but Tight) Binding to an Antibody An antibody binds to an antigen with a K_d of 5×10^{-8} M. At what concentration of antigen will θ be (a) 0.2, (b) 0.5, (c) 0.6, (d) 0.8?

8. Using Antibodies to Probe Structure-Function Relationships in Proteins A monoclonal antibody binds to G-actin but not to F-actin. What does this tell you about the epitope recognized by the antibody?

9. The Immune System and Vaccines A host organism needs time, often days, to mount an immune response against a new antigen, but memory cells permit a rapid response to pathogens previously encountered. A vaccine to protect against a particular viral infection often consists of weakened or killed virus or isolated proteins from a viral protein coat. When injected into a human patient, the vaccine generally does not cause an infection and illness, but it effectively "teaches" the immune system what the viral particles look like, stimulating the production of memory cells. On subsequent infection, these cells can bind to the virus and trigger a rapid immune response. Some pathogens, including HIV, have developed mechanisms to evade the immune system, making it difficult or impossible to develop effective vaccines against them. What strategy could a pathogen use to evade the immune system? Assume that antibodies and/or T-cell receptors are available to bind to any structure that might appear on the surface of a pathogen and that, once bound, the pathogen is destroyed.

10. How We Become a "Stiff" When a higher vertebrate dies, its muscles stiffen as they are deprived of ATP, a state called rigor mortis. Explain the molecular basis of the rigor state.

11. Sarcomeres from Another Point of View The symmetry of thick and thin filaments in a sarcomere is such that six thin filaments ordinarily surround each thick filament in a hexagonal array. Draw a cross section (transverse cut) of a myofibril at the following points: (a) at the M line; (b) through the I band; (c) through the dense region of the A band; (d) through the less dense region of the A band, adjacent to the M line (see Fig. 7–31b).

Biochemistry on the Internet

12. Lysozyme and Antibodies To fully appreciate how proteins function in a cell, it is helpful to have a three-dimensional view of how proteins interact with other cellular components. Fortunately, this is possible using the Internet and on-line protein databases. Go to the biochemistry site at

http://www.worthpublishers.com

to learn how to use the Chemscape Chime three-dimensional molecular viewing utility. You can then use the Protein Data Bank and Chemscape Chime to investigate the interactions between antibodies and antigens in more detail.

To examine the interactions between the enzyme lysozyme (Chapter 6) and the Fab portion of the anti-lysozyme antibody, go to the Protein Data Bank Website. Use the PDB identifier 1FDL to retrieve the data page for the IgG1 Fab Fragment-Lysozyme Complex (antibody-antigen complex). Open the structure using Chemscape Chime, and use the different viewing options to answer the following questions:

(a) Which chains in the three-dimensional model correspond to the antibody fragment and which correspond to the antigen, lysozyme?

(b) What secondary structure predominates in this Fab fragment?

(c) How many amino acid residues are in the heavy and light chains of the Fab fragment and in lysozyme? Estimate the percentage of the lysozyme that interacts with the antigen-binding site of the antibody fragment.

(d) Identify the specific amino acid residues in lysozyme and in the variable regions of the heavy and light chains that appear to be situated at the antigen-antibody interface. Are the residues contiguous in the primary sequence of the polypeptide chain?

Abbreviated Solutions to Problems

Chapter 6

1. **(a)** Shorter bonds are stronger and have a higher bond order (are multiple rather than single). The C—N bond is stronger than a single bond and is midway between a single and a double bond in character. **(b)** Rotation about the peptide bond is difficult at physiological temperatures because of its partial double-bond character.

2. **(a)** The principal structural units in the wool fiber polypeptides are successive turns of the α helix, which are spaced at 5.4 Å intervals. Steaming and stretching the fiber yields an extended polypeptide chain with the β conformation, in which the distance between adjacent R groups is about 7.0 Å. As the polypeptide reassumes an α-helical structure, the fiber shrinks. **(b)** Wool shrinks when polypeptide chains are converted from the extended conformation (β-pleated sheet) to the α-helical conformation in the presence of heat. The β-pleated sheets of silk, with their small, closely packed amino acid side chains, are more stable than those of wool.

3. About 43 peptide bonds per second

4. At pHs above 6, the carboxyl groups of poly(Glu) become deprotonated; repulsion among the negatively charged carboxylate groups leads to unfolding. Similarly, at pHs below 9, the amino groups of poly(Lys) become protonated; repulsion among these positively charged groups also leads to unfolding.

5. **(a)** Disulfide bonds are covalent bonds, which are much stronger than the noncovalent interactions that stabilize most proteins. They cross-link protein chains, increasing their stiffness, mechanical strength, and hardness. **(b)** Cystine residues (disulfide bonds) prevent the complete unfolding of the protein.

6. **(a)** Bends are most likely at residues 7 and 19; Pro residues in the cis configuration accommodate turns well. **(b)** The Cys residues at positions 13 and 24 can form disulfide bonds. **(c)** External surface: polar and charged residues (Asp, Gln, Lys); interior: nonpolar and aliphatic residues (Ala, Ile); Thr, though polar, has a hydropathy index near zero and thus can be found either on the external surface or interior of the protein.

7. 30 amino acid residues; 89%

8. The bacterial enzyme (a collagenase) can destroy the connective-tissue barrier of the host, allowing the bacterium to invade the host tissues. Bacteria do not contain collagen.

9. **(a)** Calculating the number of moles of DNP-valine formed per mole of protein gives the number of amino termini and thus the number of polypeptide chains. **(b)** 4 **(c)** Different chains would likely run as discrete bands on an SDS-polyacrylamide gel.

10. **(a)** NF-κ-B transcription factor **(b)** You will obtain similar results, but with additional related proteins listed. **(c)** The protein has two subunits, a p65 form (A chain) and a p50 form (B chain), which interact to form a heterodimer (quaternary structure). **(d)** The NF-κ-B transcription factor is a heterodimer that binds specific DNA sequences, enhancing transcription of immunoglobulin genes of the kappa class, from which this nuclear factor gets its name.

Chapter 7

1. Protein B has a higher affinity for ligand X; it will be half-saturated at a much lower concentration of X than will protein A. Protein A has a K_a of 10^6 m^{-1}. *Protein B has a K_a of 10^9 m^{-1}.*

2. All three have $n_H < 1.0$. Apparent negative cooperativity in ligand binding can be caused by the presence of two or more types of ligand-binding sites with different affinities for the ligand on the same or different proteins in the same solution. Apparent negative cooperativity is also commonly observed in heterogeneous protein preparations. There are few well-documented cases of true negative cooperativity.

3. Effect on myoglobin's affinity for O_2: (a) none; (b) none; (c) none. Effect on hemoglobin's affinity for O_2: (a) decreases; (b) increases; (c) decreases.

4. The cooperative behavior of hemoglobin arises from subunit interactions.

5. **(a)** The observation that hemoglobin A (HbA; maternal) is only 33% saturated when the pO_2 is 4 kPa, while hemoglobin F (HbF; fetal) is 58% saturated under the same physiological conditions, indicates that the O_2 affinity of HbF is higher than that of HbA. **(b)** The higher O_2 affinity of HbF assures that oxygen will flow from maternal blood to fetal blood in the placenta. Fetal blood approaches full saturation where the O_2 affinity of HbA is low. **(c)** The observation that the O_2-saturation curve of HbA undergoes a larger shift on BPG binding than does that of HbF suggests that HbA binds BPG more tightly than does HbF. Differential binding of BPG to the two hemoglobins may determine the difference in their O_2 affinities.

6. **(a)** Hb Memphis **(b)** HbS, Hb Milwaukee, Hb Providence, maybe Hb Cowtown **(c)** Hb Providence

7. (a) 1.25×10^{-8} m **(b)** 5×10^{-8} m **(c)** 7.5×10^{-8} m
(d) 2×10^{-7} m. Note that a rearrangement of Eqn 7−8
gives $[L] = \theta K_d/(1-\theta)$.

8. The epitope is likely to be a structure that is buried when
G-actin polymerizes to form F-actin.

9. Many pathogens, including HIV, have evolved mechanisms by
which they can repeatedly alter the surface proteins to which
immune system components initially bind. Thus the host organism regularly faces new antigens and requires time to mount an
immune response to each one. As the immune system responds
to one variant, new variants are created.

10. Binding of ATP to myosin triggers dissociation of myosin from
the actin thin filament. In the absence of ATP, actin and myosin
bind tightly to each other.

11.

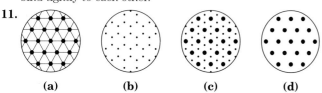

      (a)   **(b)**   **(c)**   **(d)**

12. (a) Chain L is the light chain and chain H is the heavy chain of
the Fab fragment of this antibody molecule. Chain Y is
lysozyme.

(b) b Structure is predominant in the variable and constant
regions of the fragment.

(c) Fab heavy-chain fragment, 218 amino acid residues; light-
chain fragment, 214 residues; lysozyme, 129 residues. Less than
15% of the lysozyme molecule is in contact with the Fab fragment.

(d) In the H chain, the residues that appear to be in contact
with lysozyme include $Gly^{31}, Tyr^{32}, Arg^{99}, Asp^{100}$, and Tyr^{101}. In
the L chain the residues that appear to be in contact with
lysozyme include $Tyr^{32}, Tyr^{49}, Tyr^{50}$, and Trp^{92}. In lysozyme,
residues $Asn^{19}, Gly^{22}, Tyr^{23}, Ser^{24}, Lys^{116}, Gly^{117}, Thr^{118}, Asp^{119}$,
Gln^{121}, and Arg^{125} appear to be situated at the antigen-antibody
interface. Not all these residues are adjacent in the primary
structure. Folding of the polypeptide chain into higher levels of
structure brings the nonconsecutive residues together to form
the antigen-binding site.